First published by S.A.K.S. Publications October 1996

S.A.K.S. Publications
42 Chatsworth Road
Hackney
London E5 OLP
ENGLAND
T: 0181 985 3041
F: 0181 985 9419

ISBN   0 9527784 0 8
A catalogue record for this book is available from the British
Library

Cover design of Mother and Child by Salome Smeaton-Russell
Illustrations by Rootz T: 0181 809 0111
Printed by Newham, Newark & Chambers T: 0171 739 2493

BURNING words
Flaming IMAGES
poems and short stories
by writers of African descent

Edited by Kadija Sesay

BURNING WORDS, FLAMING IMAGES

Chris Abani	Adisa	Joan Anim-Addo
Patience Agbabi	Uju Asika	Ama Biney
Sue Brown	Jean Buffong	Bernardine Evaristo
Angela Harvey Smith	Pete Kalu	Chukwunyere Kamalu
Hannah Kema Foday	Bev Miller	Jude the Observer
Stella Oni	Olusola Oyeleye	Alex Pascall
Leone Ross	Jacob Ross	Tumi Sephula
Kadija Sesay	Dorothea Smartt	Andria Smith
Paula Sorhaindo	Delroy Williams	

EDITOR
KADIJA SESAY

SAKS PUBLICATIONS

ACKNOWLEDGMENTS

My parents for their support. My brother Olu, who is the biggest pain - but I love him anyway. Thanks to the creator who keeps my sister Saffiattu, safe, strong, alive and well - and so keeps me safe, strong alive and well too.

To Ahmed Sheikh, whose criticism gave me the courage to publish the book that I really wanted, the way I wanted. To all the contributors who had patience and faith in me. To all my friends that I see too little of but because of their love and understanding, remain my friends regardless. For my godchildren whom I never see, I hope they gain some motivation and inspiration from my achievements. Adrian, thanks for helping me work on the cover at the last minute. For Don Kinch who first gave me the belief when I was 16, that I could be a writer and who told me that writing is not a part time job. Sixteen years later, Don, I hear you!

"Our deepest fear is not that we are inadequate. Our deepest fear is that we are powerful beyond measure. It is our light, not our darkness, that most frightens us. We ask ourselves, "Who am I to be brilliant, gorgeous, talented, fabulous?" Actually, who are you not to be? You are a child of God. Your playing small doesn't serve the world. There's nothing enlightened abut shrinking so that other people won't feel insecure around you. We are all meant to shine, as children do. We were born to make manifest the glory of God within us. It's not just in some of us, it's in everyone. And as we let our own light shine we unconsciously give other people permission to do the same. As we're liberated from our own fear, our presence automatically liberates others."

Nelson Mandela
President of South Africa

"All of my dreams and aspirations are bound to the dreams and aspirations of the Other.
I cannot be at home within myself until the Other is at home within her/himself.
If I want to get home, I must give the Other a ride."

Walter Earl Fluker
Director, National Resource Center for Ethical Leadership
Martin Luther King, Jr. Professor of Theology

Dedicated to Ian Worrell
who died in 1993
Fashion photographer, Singers showcase organiser
He never thought twice about giving the Other a ride.
"My philosophy in life is, I'm in too deep to sink, so I've got to swim.
I give life 110 percent just in case I miss something along the way."

CONTENTS

Titles in bold are stories

INTRODUCTION

To quote Sika Valery Small from *Calabash*, this book is an accessible easy read, therefore requires little detailed explanation or exploration, especially since the poems and stories included here will work on a different level for each person appealing to one, or another of our senses and emotions, reflecting different aspects of life at various times of our lives.

It is a melee of work exploring universal themes from a broad range of writers currently living in England, revealing their own perspectives and styles as well as providing a window for new writers and supported through a viable space for those already established.

Burning Words, Flaming Images does not profess to be the 'best in Black British literature' yet neither is it Black literature as narrowly categorised by the mainstream, highlighted by the fact that the categories they have been placed in are very loose as few of them are about one particular subject. They often incorporate different perspectives in life, such as Patience Agbabi's, *The Black, The White and The Blue*.

The use of song titles to thematise these categories was a naturally easy way to explore this divergence, especially since the link between words and music is so close. Agbabi says much the same in her writers' profile,

"I rarely differentiate between poetry and music - for me poetry is music."

And so does novelist Walter Mosley, "Music is writing and writing is music...for anyone from an oral tradition their music is in the language."

The collection was produced as a gate to walk through, explore and find what some of the best writers and some of the best writers-in-progress are moving towards.

Even as this anthology was being completed, previously unpublished writers were in the process of having their own novels and collections published: Patience Agbabi, Leone Ross and Bernardine Evaristo.

At the same time, we were conscious not to exclude what may be seen as solely performance poetry which has its place between the pages too, work from those such as Chukwunyere Kamalu, Adisa, Jude the Observer and Sue Brown.

These and the other writers included here, continue to develop their work and style - this is what distinguishes them - they consistently work hard at their writing and performance. Kwame Dawes makes this comparison with musicians when he says, Miles, Marsalis and Monk are good not because they are innovative, but they are able to be innovative because they are brilliant technically.

This will become increasingly evident as the volumes develop over the next few years with these and other writers, providing new and strong voices into the next century. As each volume comes into being, expect to see the new writers grow and become firmly rooted in the realm of established writers - new voices from writers of African descent.

The other side of the equation is that much hard work has been put into compiling this anthology and SAKS Publications has been commended on gathering these writers together. So should a previous collection of new writings by Africans living in Britain, *Sojourners*, published by the African Refugee Publishing Collective in 1984, edited by Olu Oguibe.

The sad part about it is that neither of these anthologies needed to have been viewed as 'an amazing achievement' and people should not be awed. On the contrary, it should have been easy, because every writer of African descent should have been working to make it happen. Not only because it makes it easier but it should be considered as more of an achievement if everyone plays their part to make it happen as a matter of course. What is amazing is that it doesn't happen more often, that more people don't work to make it happen. The achievements then can only be bigger, more widespread, more groundbreaking and more beneficial for everyone concerned - whilst still retaining the quality of the work. Making this process so difficult for ourselves is what is amazing, since we repeatedly acknowledge the fact that no-one else is going to do it for us in the way we want it to be done.

Kadija Sesay
October 1996

GUIDANCE

Father, dear Father; I ask for your blessings
Bless me, dear father, with knowledge and understanding.
Help me to explore, endure and fulfil the wishes
Which you so desire, through God's grace.
Enlighten me with your gift of wisdom
So that in my endeavours to find truth,
Friendship, sustenance and true companionship,
I will fulfil life's hopes and our aspirations
In the image and likeness of the tradition you so command.

Father, dear Father; giver of life and maker of all things,
Grant unto the righteous nourishment for spiritual fulfilment.
be merciful and watchful over all: elders, parents
Relatives and friends, the weak and infirm.
Sustain them with continued love and confidence.
Bless, preserve and comfort those who care.
Bestow on them your will to share thy gift of life.

Father, dear Father; whether we are near or far away,
Keep us all in constant thoughtfulness.
Remove from the path of self-righteousness
The evils of jealousy, hatred, bitterness and pain.
Turn the darkness of death into new life.
Land of my birth, may the ancestral spirits
Shield and preserve thy image; be fertile.
You cradled us all in the womb of maternal infancy
help us to follow your path with steadfastness until eternity.
Guide us all in your footsteps, through light and darkness,
Whether on land or sea, in peril or adversity

Father, dear Father; I ask of you
A father's blessing,
Guidance.

Alex Pascall OBE

1

FIRST EARRINGS

At ten, her ears were pierced
in a large department store,
shiny counters reassuring her mother
on matters of hygiene.

The assistant's thin hand
pointed the gun
at the tiny spot
a mere dot in black biro.

She fired the studs of stars
wearing, a frozen moment,
a sort of a ghostly smile
and her pale hands shook.

Those plastic gloved hands
were not grandmother's hands
with needle, and cork
and strong thread

For first earrings
binding girls to mothers
in that infinite maternal chain
criss-crossing half the world.

Each time she'd returned
to the maternal home
voices asked
"Ears not pierced yet?"

Now one more daughter belongs.
She looks deep into the mirror
and she smiles
stars.

Joan Anim-Addo

THE WHEELBARROW WOMAN

Pushed

                        pulled

       battered

                       filled.

Stomach upturned

                       emptied

legs tugged

                         up, down

             right left;

Enough!

                  No!

       No More!

That battered body

             enhanced by the toughened back

that head that was always bowed

                 now points to the sky.

That wheelbarrow woman

            now plans her own destiny.

No more

                    pushed

no more

             pulled

No more

                 filled

              and emptied at will

This woman is reborn.

                  DETERMINED IS HER NAME

Jean Buffong

milk dreams

I
dripping milk
your mouth knows
only warmth comfort
and the sensation
of the breathing
heaving chest
mellows you
your mother
spreads herself
before you
you cannot take her in
all at once
your head rolls off
and you are dreaming dreams
of her womb
still waters
still caressing you

II
mum is that you?
last night you came
back standing in the hall
your front
in your bedroom doorway
you stood naked
at the foot of the bed
spilling milk

and your daughter said
-stupid like you didn't know-
mum you haven't got any clothes on
you gave her one look
to close her mouth
but her thoughts still repeating
over and over looking frowning
until she got up
facing your naked back down
stairs to the kitchen
now in your blue white overalls
taking your girl outside to a yard
where there was none
and a big basin
water warm from a jamaican sun
looking at her
she was supposed to know
you wanted her
now unsure of herself
reassured in sweet smelling nutmeg
and handling milk
she thought she would drink
you pour it over her head
to spill down her face
pouring large
over your daughters naked body to dry
in the sun she woke up
to the sweetspice smell
of your just-baked cakes
still - hanging around her
reassured and ready

Dorothea Smartt

ole ooman

warm in a belly ol

out tru a mammy ole

into di worl ole

titty in yu mout ole

mess from yu areseole

tears from yu yeye ole

laughta from yu smile ole

eere roun yu precious ole

an in yu armpit ole

peayn roun yu nipple ole

tongue in you mout ole

an douwn yu troat ole

han' in yu bra ole

inga tru yu draarse ole

)ve in yu body ole

ief in yu treasure ole

baby in yu belly ole

tearin tru yu fanny ole

nipple in dem mout ole

wipin dem batty ole

willy in yu pussy ole

joy in yu body ole

baby in yu belly ole

bursin tru yu mammy ole

titty in dem mout ole

wipin dem rarse ole

love fi yu fambily ole

seizin up yu brain ole

centa ah yu life ol

fillin up yu ol

life!

Part ah yu ole self

Nat all ah yu ole self

Yu is yu ole self

A *yu* own all wholes

Recreate yu ole self

Ram yu in yu ole self

Den open up yu laugh ol

An sing an laugh

An shout an dance.

Andria Smith

Elevated

Our silence is not intentional.

Yet it has given us a strength that,
cannot be destroyed.

Survival through pain.
Suffering indignity.
Swallowing disregard,

has given us the gift of an
invisible coat.

Pain has turned numb.
Pride transcends indignity.
Pressure explodes the stone of disregard,

replacing it with a power that you,
in your drunken state, are too sodden to notice.

You may not see me.
Yet my sister, once on the other side,

crossed over,
and told me, I was beautiful.

I looked in the mirror,
and saw our beauty.

And that has given me an honour, that
cannot be destroyed.

Kadija Sesay

THE TEST OF WOMANHOOD

a warm night in the village of Gilluahun (between two hills) that evening. There was an excitement in the air. Mayepe was in her room looking through her clothes to find three of the most worn out dresses that she had because she had been told to do so by her mother. She could hear her and her other three mothers singing outside in the kitchen as they were cooking the evening meal. They were excited because the time had finally come for Mayepe to become a 'woman' a *Sande nyahin*. Mayepe was excited too, but she kept telling herself to keep calm because she knew she had a long and weary task ahead of her. She knew she had to prove herself to everyone before she could become a woman. She had been waiting too long for this moment to come and now it was finally here. Her friends Kony and Sebatu had been initiated over the last harvest season and she thought they now had airs about them. They did not share all of their secrets with her anymore because she was a *Kpowe* or 'uninitiated'. Mayepe thought to herself that soon they would all be equals again.

Mayepe was a beautiful fourteen year old Mende girl. She was what one would call brown-skinned and she had huge light brown eyes, a pert nose and full brown lips which contrasted very well with the tone of her skin. When she smiled, you could see two very deep dimples in her cheeks. She was tall and slender and had large shoulders so clothes fitted her perfectly. She had nice long thighs and her hips gently swayed when she walked. This made the boys go wild because when they swayed, her buttocks shook and African men love buttocks. Mayepe was not the village beauty but she knew she could hold her own amongst the beautiful girls in the village. In fact, she knew that after her initiation into womanhood, a lot of the village men, both old and young alike, would die to make her their wife.

Mayepe finally picked two worn out dresses and her favourite *lappa* or 'wrapper' to wear with them. She wished she did not have to take her nice lappa because after the initiation she knew that everything she owned would be taken away from her by the *Sowes* (the 'officials' of the Sande society). Suddenly outside she heard more singing but this time it was not in her own compound. As the singing drew closer, she knew that the Sowes were coming for her.

"Mayepe", her mother shouted, "come out of the house right now, its time for you to go."

Mayepe quickly put her clothing into a plastic bag and came out. Outside there was a huge crowd and she could see the other girls that were to be initiated standing in a long line. As she came out, everyone started singing more loudly than ever. Others were screaming, "Yeeheeheeheehee." She could see her friends Senya and Sebatu and they were cheering her on.

One of the Sowes took her bag of clothes from her and told her to say good-bye to her father.

Mayepe's father, Kini Kpana, was resting in his hammock as he usually did every evening. She went up to him and he looked at her with a solemn look on his face and said, "be brave my daughter and please come back". These words made Mayepe afraid. Why would her father say something like that to her? She remembered that a friend had once told her that initiation was very painful and they they were going to cut off something 'down there'. She had not believed that that was possible and she had asked Sebatu and Konya, but they had only laughed, saying that that was ridiculous. They told Mayepe that if anything were cut off down here, the person would surely die. Mayepe believed them. They had told her what had really happened to them, anyway.

One of the Sowes told Mayepe to lead the group of girls since she was going to be the Kema . . . . the 'first' to be initiated. Mayepe was ready. They were going to sleep in the initiation bush that night and the next morning they were to begin their test of womanhood. The whole process was supposed to last three weeks. Even though Mayepe had never seen a horse before, much less even ridden one she was ready to ride her horse to the river: a river which she would have to cross on a long thin rope. Sebatu had told her to be very careful on the rope because if she fell into the water before she finished crossing, she would be considered a witch. Mayepe was not worried about that because she knew she was not a witch. The only thing she was worried about was the crab at the end of this test of womanhood. Her friends had told her that after crossing, she had to put her hand in the river and try to get something out. Before she could get whatever it was, she would be bitten hard by the crab that guarded this thing. They told her that it hurt so much that her wounds would not have healed even after three weeks and also that she had to be very courageous or she could lose her life. "I have to be brave", Mayepe told herself. She knew she had an edge over the other girls because she knew what was in store for them. She also thought that if Sebatu and Konya had gone through this test and had not died, then she was determined to live. It was a comfort also to know that there were fifteen other girls who were going to go through this experience with her and she knew them all very well. There was Jattu who lived only two houses away from her, Senya, Miatta, her cousin Jeneba, Kadija and others.

Mayepe and the rest of the girls stood silently, not because they were in a straight line, but because they had been told to lower their heads and eyes to the ground. Mayepe, followed by the rest of the girls, slowly began moving towards the *Kpangui* (Sande compound) with the crowd of women that surrounded them. The women were singing and clapping along the way. The men, however, stood from afar watching. They knew this was 'womens business' and no one wanted to be given a fine. This was one time in the village when women had power. The 'Bush' was at the very end of town and a huge fence of palm fronds had been built all around it. No-one who was not initiated could go in, so when they got there everyone went in except for the younger girls who were not initiates.

Mayepe was finally inside the sacred *Kpangui*. There was one house in the compound. The front yard was cleanly swept and there were two towering trees in the front of the house which made a great shade from the sun. At the back of the house was a grove of orange trees full of ripe fruits. It was all very green and peaceful in the compound. At the back of the house was a small path which led to a stream and a huge cocoa farm owned by the Sowes. It was a very tranquil place, Mayepe thought. She knew straight away that she was going to have a good time here with her friends.

Mayepe and the other girls were taken into the main room of the house where someone had put mats on the floor. They were told to sit down with their legs stretched out in front of them and to sing. All of them sat down and began singing. They sang until their voices went hoarse. Some of the women began leaving before midnight. By 1:00a.m. everyone had left except the mothers of the initiates. They were going to stay with the girls until the next morning. There were two bedrooms in the house with four beds in each, but the mothers slept in the bedrooms and the initiates slept on the hard mud floor in the main room. Mayepe and the other girls could not sleep. They kept wondering amongst themselves what was going to happen to them later that morning.

****

Mayepe was quiet and Jeneba asked, "is anything wrong, cousin?"

Mayepe answered, "no."

"Are you afraid?" Jeneba asked again

"A little bit," Mayepe said.

"We all are too," said Jeneba.

"Do you know who the head Sowe is?" Mayepe asked Jattu with a questioned look on her face.

"I don't think we are supposed to see her until tomorrow."

From across the room, Miatta whispered,

"I hear she is very strict and stern and also very ugly."

All the girls started laughing which calmed them a little bit.

"Let's go to sleep, we have a long day ahead of us tomorrow and we need our rest," Senya said.

Everyone agreed and they all laid down.

Mayepe awoke from a deep sleep to someone shaking her gently. It was one of the Sowes and she had a lantern in her hand. It was still very dark out. The other Sowes were waking the other girls up. Mayepe sat up in surprise because the main room was full with about one hundred women.

Mayepe turned to Jeneba and softly said, "cousin, will we be going through our initiation with all these people watching?"

"I think so," Jeneba replied.

Mayepe's heart was beating wildly. It was still dark out and she hoped she would see the rope. The girls were told to stand in a line as they had done the night before. Most of the women were holding lanterns and they led the girls out of the house through the back door of the Bush. They walked down the footpath which led to the stream and about five hundred yards from the stream they were stopped.

A Sowe called out, "Kema!"

Mayepe answered, "na."

The Sowe said, "it's time to ride your horse."

Mayepe was then led far away from the other girls. Her heart was pounding uncontrollably in her chest. Two Sowes had come with her whilst the other Sowes had stayed behind to tend to the other girls. Mayepe looked around her and saw about one hundred women from the village standing around. She could see her 'Aunt', Ye Katumu, but her mother was nowhere to be seen.

Mayepe was told to take her clothes off. She was stunned, she thought she was going to have a heart attack.

"Take my clothes off?" she defiantly asked, "but why?"

Mayepe was definitely not going to undress in front of all these people and have all those eyes know what she looked like underneath her clothes. Sebatu and Konya had not told her that she had to be naked for the initiation. She started to resist but Ye Katumu intervened. Ye Katumu was a tall and graceful woman, a beauty in her days, and people said Mayepe looked more like her aunt than her mother. Katumu was sweet and kind to everyone and she loved Mayepe as her own child. Mayepe would trust her with her life.

Ye Katumu looked at Mayepe and said,

"Mayepe, you have to be naked to finish the test of womanhood. Your mother, I and every woman in this bush had to be naked for our initiation. We have always been proud of you and we are counting on you to finish this initiation with the strength and pride of a member of the Gevui family. So now take off your clothes like the proud daughter of Mami Gevui and start your initiation and remember that I will be at your side through it all."

Mayepe slowly took off her clothes until she was completely naked. There was not one woman that did not admire Mayepe's body. She looked majestic adorned only by her natural beauty. One of the Sowes took a piece of cloth and tied it around Mayepe's eyes. This was another surprise for Mayepe because her friends had not told her that she would be blindfolded. She wondered what else they had not told her. How was she going to see the rope if she could not see? How was she going to ride the horse? She asked those questions aloud and she was told by the Sowe not to worry. The Sowe told her she would know what to do when the time came.

Mayepe slowly felt two pairs of hands gently raise her up and put her on the back of the horse. She wished she could see this horse as she had never seen one in her life before. Its back felt so smooth and warm. She felt the horse move. She had no idea where she was being taken. Suddenly Mayepe and the horse came to a halt and, once again, she felt the same pairs of hands gently take her off the horse.

The time had come to cross the river. There was tension in the air. Mayepe knew that there were a lot of women around her, yet she could not hear even the faintest whisper. This made her uncomfortable. Why was everyone so quiet all of a sudden? Out of the quietness, Mayepe heard Aunt Katumu's voice.

"Mayepe it is time to cross the river. Don't be afraid, the head Sowe is waiting for you on the other side."

Mayepe felt her body turn to jelly. She began to tremble and she feared her legs would give way. She slowly put her feet out in front of her and felt for the bridge.

She crossed! Mayepe could not believe it. By now her heart was beating faster than ever before. She had one thought in mind. The crab. She could feel the hands of the head Sowe as she slowly helped her off the bridge. Suddenly the Sowe made an unexpected move, grabbing Mayepe's hand and thrusting it into the river. She felt the first pang of pain, it was as if her heart had been ripped out! The pain was so unbearable that her whole body went into shock. The crab continued biting. She thoughts she was going to die.

In the midst of all the pain, Mayepe could hear the women singing at the top of their voices. She realised that she was screaming loudly and that they were singing to cover her cries. Her screams could not stop. Her aunt told her to stop, but the pain was too great! Her aunt held her other hand to comfort her but Mayepe was alone in her pain.

Suddenly, just as it had begun, in a flash of confusion it was over. The crab had let go of her hand, but Mayepe felt as though she were still in the crab's claw. The head Sowe told her to get up. She told Mayepe that she had found what she was looking for in the water. Mayepe was finally a woman.

The blindfold was taken off her eyes and she could see once more, but Mayepe did not have the energy to get up. Some women had to carry her and lay her down on one of the mats that had been put under some trees. She closed her eyes because she felt as if she were going to faint. What an experience, Mayepe thought. She remembered that all the other girls would soon go through the same thing and she prayed for them. No wonder there was so much bonding between women in the village Mayepe thought, especially during initiation. She now realised that she had become part of the bond but the most important bond of all was going to be between Mayepe and the other fifteen women.

"Mayepe," she heard the soft voice of her mother calling her. She opened her eyes and saw her mother's gentle face full of tears.

"Congratulations, my daughter, you are now a *Sande nyahin*. You and I can now talk as equals."

The passage into womanhood was more painful and less fun than she had been made to believe. As Mayepe lay bleeding and weak, she began to feel betrayed by everyone she loved. But if it brought her closer to her mother, and other women, who had gone through the same experience, then it was worth it. Suddenly, another surge of pain shocked her body. Then again, she thought, maybe it wasn't.

Hannah Kema Foday

BLUES SINGERS

Blues singers.
You strip the skin from my skeleton
then smooth it on once more
cinnamon crumbled raw - blending dusk and shadow
Peeling the light that hides the musky flesh of night

Blues singers
You pull me under
nudging my soul
re-defining my centre
Filling my hollows with scoops of sound

Blues singers
you sing an ocean
tumble drown
Rebirth profound

You show me
how to reach lower
feeling deep
without feeling down

you show me
how to skim rock bottom
without hitting it

Blues Singers.

Uju Asika

BACK STAGE PARTY

Silent figures skulking
down the theatre aisles,
warning of the nearing end
of stage performance smiles.
Push and shove, and elbow dances
becomes all the rage,
body language speaks the words,
"got to get back-stage."
Pens and programmes thrust forward
groupies grope for view,
swept aside by nasal voices;
"We're friends can we come through?"
Opportunists oil their tongues,
who's who takes upper hand,
ushers puff out puny chests,
the pecking order stands;
Critics, the privileged, the chosen, the okay,
make their way to meet the
performing artist of the day.
No chance for the bashful, the stutterers, the meek
but onward go the brash
into the back stage party suite.

Choruses of "loved the show"
announce the artiste's entrance.
Friends of friends of friends
compete for stories of remembrance.
Gnashing teeth, and skittish glances
jostle for attention,
girls muster sparkles in their eyes
eager for a mention.
Urgent hands haul newest talents
to get an introduction,
intimidation quelled by hope
finds no promises, no options.
Wannabees insist they are
the most devoted fans,
whilst leather clad slicksters
drain ungaurded lager cans.
Heat, wine, cheese and farts,
smoke and stale perfume,
gather in the name of art
in the back-stage party room.

**Angela
Harvey-Smith**

DE MUSIC MAN
(cuz UB40 didn't invent reggae)

I is de music man,
I is de music,
watching blue eyed soul
mock blue notes
on gleaming white pages.

I is de music man,
I is de music,
watching pale imitations
of black music notes,
pretending to extend.

Yuh see,
dey wasn't dere
when slave whips
crack black backs
causing painful shrieks
on saxophones,
so Harry Connick Jr.,
what de hell you know
'bout jazz music?

Yuh see
dey wasn't dere
picking blues
from cottonfields,
as twelve-bar grief
vibrate from plantations,
so Eric Clapton,
what de hell you know
'bout blues music?

Yuh see
det wasn't dere
when four children feed
from half-pound of flour
in Trenchtown,
as sound-system soapbox
blast revolyrics at
isms and schisms,
so UB40,
what de hell you know
'bout reggae music?

Yuh see
dey wasn't dere
when being broke
pluck notes
from throats
dat could only
afford a song,
when riddims
was de only cure
for empty bellies
and shabby clothes,
so Simply Red
what de hell you know
'bout soul music?

but I know
I was dere,
I didn't see yuh,
don't lie,
yuh wasn't dere
I is de music man
I is de music,
I is de music man
I is de music.....

and yuh is a dam' thief.

Roger Robinson

19

JAZZ JAMAICA

What is Reggae and Jazz
Our experiences we share
Not to give away!

What is Jazz
    A Rhythm of Blues

                What is Reggae
                    A beat in the womb

What is Jazz
    An individual in collection

                What is Reggae
                    A spirit in conception

JAZZ JAMAICA

What is Jazz
    A style of passion

                What is Reggae
                    A story being told

What is Jazz
    A warmth from cold

                What is Reggae
                    A relation to the soul

JAZZ JAMAICA

What is Jazz
    The sadness of joy

                What is Reggae
                    The joy through sadness

What is Jazz
    A vision in parallel

                What is Reggae
                    A parallel in Jazz

What is Reggae and Jazz
Our experience to share
Not ever to give away.

Sue Brown

MUSICIAN IN FLIGHT

A musician in flight is
an instrument of his instrument.
Impelled to revel in spiritual employ
until climax releases him totally spent,
and he opens his eyes to
rejoin mortal rank.

Angela Harvey-Smith

JAZZ PETALS

"My Jasmine baby," my mother had called me when I first popped my head out from between her legs all blood and screams. My Dad, who was very liberated and so a source of constant embarrassment to my mother, swears the delivery room was filled with the soft sweet suffusal of jasmine. That's how I got my name. But then I shortened it to 'Jas' and spelt it 'Jazz'. I think from then on I became a disappointment to my mother. Mum says I was born delicate and had nearly translucent skin but then as I got older I became stocky and dark. I was not going to be the great beauty my mother had hoped for, her jasmine plant.

I have dim memories from early childhood. Dim because they are faded out of focus like a well thumbed photograph or those sepia prints of the nineteenth century you see in Tesco supermarkets. They were more like shards of memory if there is such a thing. My mother washing my hair, oiling it, combing it, stretching it, teaching me to cook. The act always differs but the same basic thread of mother-daughter bonding runs through it all. The memories of our mothers are etched on our bodies. A song, a recipe, washing our hair, playing with dolls. Men seem to bond differently. They project onto objects - footballs, cars, guns, girls.

My mother was an adept of subliminal programming. While she did my hair, or bathed me, or let me help in the kitchen - whenever we were together - she would sing the litany of womanhood to me. Sloughed off snatches of which, still whisper in my ear even as I sleep causing me to wake up sweating.

"What better way to please a man than to spice his food with the essence of our love, with the sweetness of our joy and the sharpness of our sorrow and sacrifice."

"Remember, Jasmine. Women take their pleasure from pleasing their men."

"Good little girls always listen to their parents."

"A good woman keeps her virginity until marriage."

"Spinsterhood is death. No, death is preferable."

Over and over I learnt the age old recipe for women's oppression. Sung by women but the words written by men. Always by men. But there was always a level of my soul I could retreat to where the words couldn't reach me. I felt my mother envy and fear me for this.

My father loved John Coltrane. I must have been seven or eight when I first remember hearing the soulful breathing of his saxophone. It moaned and cried and sang and laughed. It moved me first to tears, then laughter. It left me breathless and aroused. Later there were others - Miles Davis, Stanley

Turrentine, Joe Henderson, Cannonball Adderly, the bird - Charlie Parker. The soft growl of the sax was like a hunger in my belly and it crawled all over my skin leaving snake trails of sensation, arousing senses I did not understand but love. Yet somewhere the voice of my mother, would creep in and I would flush. This often only served to amplify the sensation making me light headed and giddy. I would feel the petals unfurl between my legs as a moist sweetness tingled there. I called them petals before I knew what a labia was. I still call them petals, my Jazz petals.

When I was twelve, I decided I wanted to take up the sax.

"Sax is not lady-like," mother sang. "Better for you is ballet."

But Dad thought she should leave me alone to make my own choices.

"You are spoiling that girl," mother ranted at him. "I hope you will live the shame of a spinster daughter with no shelf life left."

Dad never said much. Yet in his silence he often had his way.

"All that music," mother went on, "leads only to temptation and babies. It's unnatural the way that music creeps inside you and stirs your fantasies."

Dad didn't argue and we went to get a sax, anyway.

"Start her with an alto," the shop assistant advised, "the tenor has a deeper pitch and bigger bell not suitable for a young girl"

Dad looked at me.

"I want the tenor Dad."

He looked deep in my eyes and recognised the determined glint there.

He turned back to the assistant.

"We'll take the tenor." Dad told the assistant.

And so the laborious process of lessons and practice began. Mum hated every second it.

"She sounds like she's summoning evil spirits," mother whispered.

Dad smiled. "She'll get better."

"All day she's up in her room. Blow, blow, blow. No time for friends. No time for cooking, cleaning. She will not find a husband," mother sang. "She will be under your roof for the rest of her life, blowing your shame on that blasted horn. A totally unnatural business."

I guess I've always found lips attractive. Lips, sucking, tonguing and blowing on my sax mouthpiece became erotic. The reed became my clitoris. As I blew, my petals unfolded and warm juices flowed. I would blow and flow in a continuous stream. I was very sexual at twelve. I was not conscious of it, but I certainly felt it.

Once on a school trip to the zoo I got really friendly with Angela. We sat next to each other and talked all the way. We laughed with the hyenas together. Tried to tickle the monkeys and feed the animals anyway, ignoring the sign that said PLEASE DO NOT FEED THE ANIMALS. We felt daring. We felt bad. The thrill was great. We became firm friends from then on. We both liked jazz and she played the piano. We didn't seem to have much interest in boys and yet we both burned with a strange sexual fire. We went everywhere together. We slept over at each others houses all the time.

My mother seemed happy with me for the first time in my life. She absolutely loved Angela.

"She is a good girl," she would say. "Perhaps you can learn some of her reserve."

Reserve? Angela? If only she knew. Angela was the wilder of us both. But she had a certain chameleon quality that I lacked. She could make herself blend into any background. She was, when she was around my mother, the daughter she had never had in me. That was when I first realised just how much of a disappointment I really was to my mother. I have come to make that the theme of our relationship when I later took up sky diving, formed an all woman jazz band, took my pilot's license and wore jeans all the time. But all that would only come later when I left University and home.

Once, when we were fourteen, I went to Brighton for the weekend with Angela and her parents. One night I had a nightmare. I switched on the bedside lamp and calling softly to her I climbed into bed next to her. She tried to soothe me. Her hands, little white butterflies, fluttered all over my body. At first she just touched my face and hair, but then turning adventurous, they roved down to my breasts and my nipples hardened. A soft moan escaped from me Then her hands moved even further down tracing sigils down my body evoking a a deep desire. My petals unfurled as her breath kissed my lips. The night air was heavy with the heady aroma of jasmine. It seemed to leak from my skin as though everywhere she touched me, she ripped great big gaping holes. That night seemed to go on forever.

The next day we returned to London. We never told anyone else about it, keeping it our secret. But then we were no longer just friends. Something deeper left its shadow and in the daylight, in London, we were afraid of shadows. And so we went to great trouble to pretend it had never happened. We talked only of boys, clothes and jazz. We drifted apart. Angela never slept over at my house anymore. My mother was too angry to speak more than one sentence to me.

"Ruin your life. See if I care."

I was convinced my Dad could read what had happened from my face. We never kept secrets from each other and I never lied to him. I dreaded him asking me anything. Finally, three weeks later on the landing, as we passed each other he said casually,

"Your playing is different."

"How do you mean?" I asked, my heart thumping.

"You seem less hungry now. More sated. More sensual," he said.

"Oh?"

"Listen, Jazz, you can tell me anything you know." Dad began.

"Like what Dad?" I asked, sounding casual and blase.

"Did you sleep with a boy in Brighton," he asked

I was relieved. This way I wouldn't have to lie. Not as if he had asked, "are you still a virgin?"

"No Dad," I said.

Suddenly he seemed embarrassed. He muttered something and walked on.

****

All through University, I led a double life. I felt that it was the least I owed my mother for being such a disappointment to her. To protect her from the truth, I kept my long hair although I secretly desired a crew cut and had done so since I was eighteen. Yeah, a purple crew cut - what a stage presence! I still wore make-up, even though my face came up in a fine rash. My finger nails were a long shocking red that pleased my mother because it made me look 'straight' to her.

I was really unhappy and was often depressed. At first mother thought I was pregnant. All the classic symptoms she said. But when I didn't break out into morning sickness and a big tummy she gave up on the pregnancy angle and decided to play agony mum. My life then became full of phrases like,

"Don't worry. A nice young man will soon come along."

"It's not how long you wait, but the quality of what you get."

I planned my own death. Should I be boring and just slash my wrists or take the painless approach, you know with tablets. But the thought of making a mistake and not dying kept me up nights. Living to face the prospect of my mother watching and nagging me soon put me off that idea. But I kept planning to do something really radical to show my parents not just who I was but why I couldn't keep living their life.

I even had strange dream sequences with Coltrane, or Trane as I came to know him. We always met in old world jazz bars. The ambience was always perfect. It would be pouring with rain outside but warm and cosy inside. We were usually alone as we were rehearsing for a gig. He had a slow, low and very laid back voice filled with smoke cracked experience.

"What's troubling you, Jazz," he asked.

And I would blurt out my woes.

"So what's the problem? You know you've got to be true to yourself when you play the tenor or the notes come out all wrong and the song sounds bad. Some of the best music comes from your pain as a musician."

"So?"

"So take all that anger and frustration inside out and sing the blues, baby. Make those notes ring with feeling. Besides, it's cheaper than therapy."

And his smoky laugh would fill my soul. I cherished those dreams.

One day, I was cooking at home for Dad. Mum was over at Aunty Aktar's. I looked up and out of the window over the sink. In the soft light of dusk I saw a stranger's face reflected back at me. She had long hair, mascaraed eyelashes, a gash for a mouth. I was so shocked I dropped the plate I was washing.

"Are you alright?" Dad called out.

"Fine." I mumbled.

I reached for the sharp paring knife by the side and grabbing a fistful of my hair I hacked it off. I kept hacking away, the hair piling up by my feet, until I had a rough crew cut. I then reached into the cupboard above my head and took out my mother's favourite set of ten crystal dishes with lids. I rushed upstairs and grabbed a tampon, my lipstick - cherry red I think it was, a pair of frilly knickers, red nail polish and a picture of Tom Cruise torn out of a magazine. I rushed back into the kitchen. I put each of the items into a dish and covered it. Then I put some locks of my hair into another, some whole dried chilli's into another, rice, a washing up glove and nail clippings into the last one. Bright red still, they looked like drops of dried blood. I arranged the dishes on the kitchen table in a strange sort of pyramid. My life, as prescribed by mother, preserved mummy-like for her. I could no longer afford the luxury of a doplleganger. By the time Mum came home I was a shocking blond crew cut dyke.

"Why? Why?" mother sang.

Dad looked all crumpled and creased like an empty cigarette packet. I suddenly wished I hadn't decided to tell them I was a lesbian. What with the desecration of my mother's dishes, it all seemed too much. But I pressed on.

"Don't you see?" I asked incredulous.

"Do you want to shock us?" mother sang.

"No! I want to be me." Even as I said it, the line sounded so corny. But sometimes when we voice the profundity of our souls it does sound corny we are all so afraid to let each other close.

"Didn't we love you enough? Or perhaps too much?" Dad is almost talking to himself.

"Why? Why Jas?" Mother's litany is beginning to irritate more than usual.

"Why am I a lesbian? I don't know. I was born that way. I like being that way. Ever since I was a child I have been this way. Isn't it enough that I am?"

I wanted to explain about the jazz petals and the lips and Coltrane but I thought they'd been shocked enough.

Dad turned away from me and the look in his eyes broke my heart. I wanted to be his little girl again. To have him love me unconditionally. Feel his bristly chin brush against my soft cheek. But I knew that those images belonged to another time and place.

"I should have brought you an alto saxophone", he whispered. "Or perhaps I shouldn't have bought you one at all."

"Why? All that lovely hair. Years it took to grow. Now you look like a plucked chicken. Why? " Mother said sitting on the floor to gaze up at my pyramid.

****

These days I am much happier. Dad seems to have forgiven me and himself. Mother continues to chant marriage spells at me trying not to look at my blue or green or orange or red or purple crew cut.

"When will you find a nice young man and settle down?" she asks.

"I am settled mum. With Lucy."

"Just you wait. I was like you - well not exactly. But I felt like you. I did not like men, at least not until I met your father. Wait. You'll see."

We have settled into a little routine. I go round to my parents house every other month to see mother. She won't come to the flat I share with Lucy. Dad I meet more often, he comes to watch me play. We share coffee. Gossip. Hours together rifling through old musty records in second hand jazz shops.

He only came to the flat once though. He stood by the CD player soaking in Coltrane, smoking his way through, 'In a Sentimental Mood,' while I made coffee.

"It wasn't me was it Jazz?", he asked as I handed him the coffee.

"No Dad."

"I'm glad," he smiled, sipping on his coffee.

Chris Abani

12.02

12.02, lonely Saturday night
we're not talking just had'da fight
no warm embrace, no holding tight

Feet tucked in, careful not to meet
though secretly wishing our lips would greet
our hips to rock in single beat

Instead we lay at distant ends
each too proud to make amends
awaiting cupid's bow to bend

Back to back, bodies rigid as stone
hearts apart, together alone.

Delroy Williams

MASK AT THE MARKET

In the shadow of the mosque we kissed,
in the darkness of the blues we moved slowly together,
at the bus stop in the early morning we talked forever,
in the African market we held each other.

"Do you love me more
than anything else in the world?" I asked.

"Yes," she said.

I caught a Yoruba mask smiling.

Pete Kalu

NEW CHILD

I

At midnight
my moist womb
pulls open
Blood flows
birth

II

New Child

born

in no
scent

no scent
baby

III

Into the light
baby
     d
      r
       a
        g
        g
         i
          n
           g
After birth.

IV

Life -
makes the noise
of
baby crying

V

My hand
o u t s r e t c h e d
bears the weight of innocence.

VI

The pram is coming
I had a kiss ready
warm hands
caress.

Olusola Oyeleye

RAINWALKING

The wind blew us together

I was clinging to
the stem of your umbrella

and we were close and
you were warm and wet

Sam's River just opening
wafts of barbecue rib

burst up my nostrils, gusted
into our lungs, but we were skint

we were hanging in the wind
dripping wet and salivating

almost home,
the wind teased scent from out of

your hair: citrus and hotdogs,
body oil and Vosene shampoo.

I muzzled into you, bit your neck,
tasted you and the rain

the rain made your face shine,
and strands of hair
stuck to your forehead and

the rest of your pageboy
cut had its geometry
stir-fried by the wind

tears in our eyes
We got back and

we were drenched and
we were famished and
we were blissed...

Pete Kalu

STARSTRUCK

Name a point at which
the star is not connected
to its dark surroundings
and i'll let u go

Delroy Williams

PHONECALL TO A
RAPE CRISIS CENTRE

The man spoke to me with his body. How could I get away from him?

We are biologically, sexually, intellectually entwined. He taught me that people matter in many ways but not others. He taught me that feeling is not a cliché. He taught me how to critique poetry how to watch people, how to give up and start again. He taught me how to perform felatio and pretended in his turn that my body was edible, hummed jazz when he sucked my toes, screamed when he climaxed and cried in his sleep. He created me for him, him for me. Somewhere in the destined thread of life, our bodies were formed to fit each other, Coffee is just coffee, but when he made it, it caressed my lips, stroked my throat and its aroma made love to me.

We had children, but only in our minds. Despite our seeming nonchalance, it did matter what people said, how they whispered that my hair was in ribbons when grey flirted with his temples, that while I was sucking my thumb he was learning to suck pussy in high school. Sometimes we hid in response to the torture around us. Sometimes we defied it, caressed in public, hips grinding, wetness spreading.

There were earlier days when he performed his God given role: teacher guide. He made sure I did my homework, bandaged my scrapes and gave me a kitten for my thirteenth birthday. At night he rolled me into a ball and tucked himself in the edges. I would bounce on his lap, like other little girls, only I was perched on the hard length of him. You see, his wife never understood him. She never understood me either, and she was my mother. The only good thing that ever came out of their marriage was me.

We do have fun.

We do.

Leone Ross

RESPECT DUE - TO WHO?
A FRIEND, THAT'S WHO

For you are a Friend and so am I
Encourage, consolidate, stimulate. invigorate
Sometimes talk
Sometimes listen
Sometimes just being there
For you are a Friend and so am I.

For you are a good Friend and so am I
With experiences we share, thoughts and pains
We embrace all the good times
Learn from the bad times
But always for better times
For you are a good friend and so am I.

For you are a best Friend and so am I
Whether or not we agree with each other
Or whether we simply acknowledge each other
Because of respect and trust,
Love and affection will always conquer
Some friends you just never lose
For you are a best friend and so am I.

For you are a true Friend and so am I
Out of strength and emotions
Expressions become impressions
To form a collective inspiration
As emblems from womankind for mankind
For you are a true friend and so am I.

Sue Brown

FOR SAMMY DAVIS JR.

Good bye Twinkle Toes.
You Ol' Buckle-Shoe, Shim-Sham-
Rap-A-Tap, Knee-Bang, Beetle-Bugging
Shuffler. Never Did Get Tired Of You.

Pete Kalu

TAKE DIS POEM
(4 murdered Stephen Lawrence mother)

Take dis poem
and dry mama tears.
Let liquid sadness
run de ink
and join de words
making dem stronger.

Take dis poem
and soak up spilt
blakk blood,
let it stain
de path of tears
in case dey dry up
and we forget.

Take dis poem
and wipe de cold sweat
of all mothers
wondering
if dey baby go
make it home
tonight.

Den take dis poem
and fly it
at de half mast of your mind.
Gaze at it like
a 3D magic eye poster,
and watch de intricacies
of racist manifestos
slowly,
slowly,
unfold.

Roger Robinson

FOR BOET PITIKA

Go well!
son of Africa
go well.

I will smile,
when I remember as a young girl
how I was in awe
of your mind,
holding on to your
great teachings on
Dialectic Materialism
and wondering
did you ever understand
what it meant!

I remember
how you would
make your presence felt
with your poetry,
dancing in time
to the beat of drums,
calling to the ancestors
to return
sons and daughters
for the struggle.
I will hold those special memories
of yesterday
close to my heart.

Go well
child of Africa
go well.
We stand on this mountain
raising our arms
to lift you up
closer to our mother.
Let the warm rays
behind the clouds
awaken your hidden dreams,
reminding you again
of that warm smile
that knows you.

Go well, Boet Pitika.
Go well.
You will not
have to play mind games
to survive,
explaining yourself
by doing it twice as hard
at every step of the way.

There will be
no glass ceiling to break
with your palms.
Stay close to mother Afrika
listen to her wisdom,
she will speak to you
late in the night
in between
her breaths of slumber
when you will hear
your answers.

Sometimes
when you look back
and hear a piece of laughter
and feel tears flow
about pain you've known
or
remember a secret shared,
an unexpected surprise,
treasure them
close to your heart.

Boet Pitika,
the pieces of our memories
can only be put together
like a tapestry,
when we meet again.

Go well,
Boet Pitika,
Hamba Kahle!
Tsamaya sentle!

*Boet is an Afrikaans word for 'big brother'/uncle.
Tumi has known Pitika Ntuli, poet and sculptor
since she was 12 years old.

Tumi Sephula

DE LAST BAPTISM
(4 A FRIEND WHO DROWNED)

Dey push you out to sea
as an offering,
De candlelight of carefreedom
glaring from your forehead.
You bubbling and swaying
with tides and tidings
dat can't crack de calabash
carrying you from shore.

Twenty-two waves away
de beacon brightness offering warm
sight,
to sandy toes,
as dey dance and sway
in your incandescent
flambeaux permeance.
Defeating nature
in a bold faced way,
Basking in a spirit
of cance taking,
riding tidal waves
with a flicking laugh.

Until de calabash crack,
drowning de flame
in a sea of unfulfilled
hopes and prayers.

De shore was never
darker than dat night.

Mooma, mooma your son
in de grave already!

Now de pain buzzing
like mosquitoes
round mi head,
Taking turns at
sucking mi lifeblood,
Every bit hurting
as much as de first,
making mi throat swell
and mi cheeks wet.
Well
dat's
how
death
does
drop
it.
Now light reflections
making me sad,
Even though
I wasn't there
at de last baptism.

Mooma, mooma your son
in de grave already
Your son in de grave already
Take a towel
and ban' your belly.

No more drinks
for de dead!

No more drinks
for de dead!

Roger Robinson

41

CELLO'S AND A HAPPY STORY

.a. That's whom the smell of Earl Grey tea reminds me of. Beata. inevitable that it always would. Ever since the first day we met. It was summer and the sweet smell of magnolia kissed the London air, jarring with the harsher perfume of car exhausts. We met in a jazz shop in Shaftesbury Avenue. I was rifling through the CD's looking for releases of old Jazz classics. Later she asked me why not vinyl. I said it reminded me of times in my life best forgotten. She was looking for sheet music written for Jazz cello. Quite rare. There's nothing quite like cello, especially when it licked through those Jazz scales. It didn't cry the blues, not like some other instruments. Not in the high pitched wail of guitars or the loud yell of trumpets, the breathlessness of saxophones. Not in the haunting whimper of the vibes or piano. It bellowed the blues. A deep rumbling inside that was your heartbeat. Your soul. Your deepest darkest pain. It used to creep under my skin and sear at the tender flesh of my soul. We often played duets. Me on the tenor sax, she on the cello. My sax would dance playfully around, teasing, its notes just out of reach of her deeper chords. But all that would come later. I smelt the brewing Earl Grey coming from the cafe next door. I looked up. She was opposite me, a wistful, longing smile played over her lips.

"Don't you just love that smell", she breathed at me.

"Sunset over the Himalayas," I breathed back. Strangely it didn't sound corny.

"Would you drink with me?" she asked.

"My pleasure."

****

"So much sadness in you," she said reading my stories. "What happened to you?"

"I don't know. I just write what the spirits channel," I answered.

"Ah," she said breaking off a quarter from a satsuma and sucking at it's juice, hardly grazing its skin. "That's different."

"Why?" I asked trying to imitate her but ripping a jagged gash in the satsuma's tender flesh.

"Because it means you are blessed."

"Really? Cursed is a better word. But why do you say blessed? " I asked intrigued.

"Really. The spirits channel healing through you. They let sad people unburden themselves through you and they let others tell their stories through you. Stories that help us all understand our essential humanity.

Only the very lucky and the very best are chosen."

"I thought every artist is chosen. What makes me so special?"

"Precisely because you are an artist. The world is full of artisans, but true artists - visionaries - they happen only every so often. You are one."

I was a bit uncomfortable with all this. She noticed and smiled, then laughed. Her laugh was the deep rumbling of a cello. This was a little surprising considering she was a little sprite of a thing. She leaned across and kissed me tenderly on the lips.

"Love yourself my friend. Love is all. Love is life. Love is happiness. And all art is love."

****

"Write me a happy story," she said.

"I don't know how," I replied.

"Sure you do," she retorted. She was sometimes a little sharp with me when she felt I was holding back from her. But her sharpness never cut. Instead it sent a series of painfully sweet tinglings through me. Reminiscent of our lovemaking.

"All you have to do is open up yourself a little. Don't be afraid to get hurt. It makes life more interesting. Take a risk. Laugh," she went on shaking her head in exasperation. I laughed. Her face lit up, "You should laugh more often," she said. "It's easy."

"Not for me, " I said.

"Yes it is. Start by writing me a happy story. No break ups. No tears. No death. No sorrow. Just happy, happy, happy. You know, like those hippie Simon and Garfunkel songs. Cher and Bono."

So I try. And try. And try. I trace patterns across the page. Happy stories. Ionie is 35. She works in an office off Upper Street. She sits by a window which slumbers in the shade of a green tree. She adores her job. Her boss is a pleasure to work for. She munches on sugary, iced and sweet doughnuts and drinks copious amounts of espresso. She doesn't add weight and the caffeine does nothing to her metabolism. She has great skin. Her hair is always perfect. She has a great husband and two lively kids and lives happily in suburbia. She belongs to a book discussion group. She favours ethnic minority writers which she thinks are hip. She drinks jasmine tea and protects the whales. She votes Labour. She has loads of credit on her cards. She is happy, happy, happy.

"What is this nonsense?" she asks throwing my story across the room. "You should be ashamed."

"I told you happy stories were boring and crappy but you would not listen."

"Pathetic excuses," she yells. "Nothing is boring if an artist touches it.

43

Even the most banal of things takes on a profundity that is awe inspiring. The only boring thing here is your story. Now go and write me a happy story."

So I start again. And again. But it sounds trite, moralistic and didactic. You know the kind: Sunday school, country music, the Waltons, Little House on the Prairie, the Brady Bunch. I don't know how to do it. I can write easily about death, murder, sadness and sorrow. But happiness, well happiness is kind of banal. And besides, happy stories ain't selling much this year.

"What makes you happy," she asks patiently as she rips up my latest attempt.

"I don't know," I say. I'm angry, petulant. Sulky. Childish.

She sighs.

"All right. Let me put it another way. Where does your happiness come from?"

"Inside."

"And your sadness?"

"Inside."

"Don't you see. They spring from the same part of you. Very often that which makes us sad is the very same thing that makes us happy."

I take a sip from my cup. I followed her, I think - but it all sounds too Khalil Gibranish to me.

She senses my uncertainty.

"Do I make you happy?" she asks.

"Of course you do," I reply wondering whether this is some female mind trick. You know, make me think we are talking about a story when all the while its about us.

"If I went away, would you be sad?" she continues.

I know the answer to that one I think. It gets easier and easier to understand people when you live with them.

"Deeply sad," I reply adopting my best puppy dog look. She doesn't even notice. At least she doesn't let on if she does.

"But if I came back then you'd be happy again, right?"

"Yes," I answer suddenly feeling like an absolute fool because I can suddenly see what she's trying to show me. We are still talking about the story. We haven't in fact talked about anything else.

"What's your earliest sad memory?" she asks me. "Tell me."

"I'm two or three," I say. "I listen to that song *where's your mama gone* all day. I fall asleep and dream that I'm alone on earth. Everything is gone. There is nothing but the refrain from the song constantly repeating: *'last night I heard my mama singing a song, ooh weee, chirpy, chirpy, cheep cheep. Woke up this morning and my mama was gone ooh weee, chirpy, chirpy, cheep cheep.* I jerk awake. I'm sweating. Screaming."

"And then what?" she probes softly, gently.

"I can smell my mother. She is kissing me. Hugging me. Shushing me back to sleep. 'There there. It's only a bad dream,' she whispers softly. I fall asleep again. No more nightmare."

I feel embarrassed suddenly.

"So you see. Happiness and sadness. Together. One from the other. Now write me a happy story."

****

The doctor's say she won't live long. Perhaps if the cancer was detected sooner, she might have survived. She asks how long exactly. They say six months, seven at most. But that's with chemotherapy they hasten to add. The consultants avoid our eyes, ashamed almost.

She refused chemotherapy. And their drugs, except for the painkillers which she said kept the wolf - like pain away.

"How does it feel," I ask trying to get inside her. To take this pain on. To share it. To do something, anything.

"You know, I fee like a flint troll, all sharp edges and knobbly pebbles," she says.

I laugh. Despite, her suffering, she still reaches out to comfort me.

"You should laugh more often," she says softly. "It's easy."

I fight the tears. She sends me away to go and finish her happy story.

"Tell it, tell it," she whispers urgently. "Tell a happy story for me."

****

I sit staring at the blank sheet of paper tucked into the typewriter. I cannot write. I reach for the vodka and try to burn my way through to some feelings but my heart is still and cold like ice.

Then suddenly she starts playing her cello. The melodic rumblings roll across the flat like waves crashing against me relentlessly. It's a classical piece. A Latin hymn set to music.

Stabat Mater. Stood the mother full of grief. It sings of Mary's feelings as she watches Jehuda die on the cross. I close my eyes. I see Mary staring up at the cross, twitching as Jehuda flinches. Her soul rips open and crows peck at her heart. Every drop of blood hits her heart, driving with the pain of a nail. The crown of thorns crushes her brow into a million fragments of pain. "My son, my son." she whispers. "Why? Why" she cries out at a silent and uncaring father. "I hate you," she screams. I'm sure I hear her. She is sadder than any words can begin to describe. John holds her gently and she resents the warmth of his living body. Why not him there on that cross. Or James. The cello doesn't let up and I can feel my self splitting in two. I moan softly. Then all of a sudden the tempo picks up. It's racy. It's happy. It's chattering away so fast I can't hear it, like a thousand sand fairies, their silicate tongues clicking as they laugh. I see Mary begin to smile. Jehuda looks down and says to her and John, "Mother behold thy child, son of thy mother." He dies. His pain is over and he soars triumphantly up to the sun. She is suddenly no longer sad and she understands why. She feels the sun raking her apart with soft rays of light and her joy is a thousand doves fluttering up to heaven. Beata stops playing. I wipe my hand across my face. It is wet with tears I am not aware of crying. I feel suddenly empty and yet full. Sated and yet burning with hunger. Joy, sorrow and laughter dance across my paper blurring into one. At last. At last a happy story begins to emerge.

****

She died a few weeks later. Three months earlier than the doctors said she would if she had been on chemotherapy. But she had all her hair. Her copper hair actually seemed to grow longer as she died. Longer and fuller, shining with health and life.

I did not mourn her. I was not sad. No Stabat lover's for me. I played 'Amazing Grace' in church on my sax. The acoustics were great. I swear she smiled. Then I walked in front of the pall bearers blaring out a medley of happy Dixie sounds. No mournful wails. Just a happy casual banter. Life was good. Beata was free. What was it she used to say, "Love is all. Love is art. Love is Life." Well as long as I loved her she lived. In every falling leaf. In every song. Everytime I heard the cello. I stood by her graveside long after everyone had left. I stood and laughed for hours. She was right. It was easy.

****

I'm married now. I have a lovely wife whom I adore and three angelic children. Life is good. I'm a successful writer. I still play sax and occasionally the cello. Yes I took lessons. I finished Beata's happy story. It in fact became my first best-seller. The heroine's name is predictably Beata.

New. Innovative. Celebrates the banality of modern suburban life. Profound. the critics said. They loved it. It is called The Hill Where The Lord Hides. Strange title. But then I'm a strange man. Stranger for having met Beata.

I think of her often. And I celebrate her life everytime I drink a cup of Earl Grey tea, which is often. But strangely, I cannot bring myself to tell my wife about her. That strange child-woman of Oa who taught me to laugh, so easily.

Chris Abani   46

ROOMS

My clothes are best friends
with the floorboards
they watch the ants
trundle by
and make mountains
fantasy lands
of lipstick reds
and greys
for them to play in

His clothes
stand on spit-
polished
parade

He pulls the bed covers
Tight
A child's plait
coins would bounce
like in hotels.

In my bed
they wait
tousled,
for more loving.

I have ten year old
sweet wrappers
love letters
cassettes that are out of date

He decorates
with aftershave
moisturizer
a weight, for God's sake.

But when he comes to my room
he smoothes the hot and thirsty
sheets
leaves his sweet
breath to linger through
the book-leaves.

When I leave his room
There are cartoons
colourful on the shelf
The carpet
warmed
His cool lips sticky

An errant
pair of my
underwear
peep crazily from a
corner
And make him laugh at night.

Leone Ross

SIMMERING

Simmering
SIM MER RING

Eyes	smouldering
Vibes	firing
Heart	pounding
Body	aching
Juices	flowing
Patience	going
Passion	flaring

Desire sounding
Senses tingling

Together	blending
Horizons	widening
Body	opening
Eagerly	receiving
Gifts	sooo pleasing
Brain	overloading
Body	exploding

My lovers supplying
All that I'm needing.

Bev Miller

OUCH

Eating tangerines through an anxious smoke-filled
room
eases the restlessness
in my throat

I don't play our love scenes
in my head any more.
Somebody took the video tape
probably for my own protection
it was overdue at the store
anyway

I don't see your face
on my pillow
quite as frequently
as I did
six months ago.
Only sometimes your tender eyes
laugh with me
from the faces of nameless joggers
and astonish me
into an ache that can last for hours

and sometimes
I waste an idle morning
smoking
through tangerines
thinking about your ass.

Leone Ross

SOCKS AND SUNGLASSES

I met a man
wearing crazy socks
purple, green, orange, yellow
all the colours of the rainbow
left me feeling warm and mellow
and I wondered if they would feel the same
worn as condoms?

From the quif on his head
to his purple toes
there is something about that man
I just unfroze - he left me steamin'.

I met a man
wearing rounded glasses,
dark, for the sun
and I wondered if his bun
would make me come
(round to his way of thinking)?

From the quif on his head
to his purple toes
there is something about that man
I just unfroze - he left me steamin'.

I met a man
chocolate and smooth
I licked, I nibbled
my water just dribbled
until the chocolate sizzled
and I wondered if we spent too long
by the fireplace?

From the quif on his head
to his purple toes
there is something about that man
I just unfroze - he left me steamin'.

He licked his lips
Then he licked mine
Give me Atlanta chocolate
An-ee-time
Because it's soft and warm and steamin'.

Kadija Sesay

52

SEX MYTHS

Cast away the bells and the crashing waves
-this is an ode to the sticky mess of sex

like how
he falls out just
when you're about to come
and it all trickles down your thigh

and how the room smells
afterwards
oysters and bitter pennies
and whipped cream
for naughty nights

One of my tits gets caught
in the fray
underneath his elbow
and he thinks I had an orgasm

He bashes my cervix and we re-think strategy

And how about the way
your thighs get tired when you're
on top
and you thought you could swallow
But have a giggling fit
and upchuck on the sheets....

Leone Ross

COOK FOR TALK.

"Auntie-eh!"

Isatu came tap-tapping on the kitchen door, loaded down with onions, tins of plum peeled tomatoes, jars of tomato puree and fresh garnish for the meat stew. She struggled in, arms stretched ready to come out of her shoulder sockets and palms sore from the plastic handles of carrier bags that left red tracks on her hands.

"Yes my dear. Eh! You carried all this load yourself! Kushe-oh! You've done well my dear. Now we have everything to finish the cook. Good girl. Rest them there."

Auntie Omo pointed her chubby wet finger to the corner by the sink. She turned back to the gas cooker, the fat of her lower arms wobbling as she ladelled the meat, marinated from the night before, into the gaping mouth of the hot cooking pot, already greedily spitting with oil. She watched satisfactorily as the spicy, peppery, smell rose, as soon as it hit the oil and immediately started to turn the red meat grey. At that sight, the kitchen became resonant with her voice.

"We are ready for the onions!"

Auntie Omo sang out in her coaxing sing - songy voice. She went to church regularly, so her voice naturally was strong. Isatu quickly and obediently removed her coat, scrambled for the huge cooking knife in the cutlery drawer and obediently began peeling, slicing and dicing the onions into tiny squares with a rhythmic chop-chop.

Femi now, was saying very little, having lodged herself comfortably on a cushioned stool between the fridge and the pot cupboard. She had a large, red plastic bowl between her hugging legs and was leisurely, almost dreamily picking the rice.

"Quickly, quickly, with these onions, eh Isatu, we don't want to still be cooking come nightfall."

"Yes, Auntie", said Isatu, trying to chop even faster, although it was hardly possible. Bits of onion flew across the kitchen floor, odd bits escaping, tossing themselves first into the air before joining the others, but anything, anything to please Auntie Omo.

"What's the baby to be called?" said Isatu trying to chat at the same time, to ease Auntie Omo into a less anxious mood.

"Brima."

"After the father!"

"Of course after the father"

"If that is the father", Femi mumbled to herself.

"What was that, Femi?"

Omo sang sharply.

Femi continued picking the rice as if she had said nothing.

"Femi?"

"What now?"

Femi abruptly stopped what she was doing and splayed her hands, as if she had been attacked unfairly.

"What are you saying about Brima Junior now?"

"I don't need to repeat it. You know anyway." She raised her head. "You're the one who told me." She carried on in her lazy droning fashion.

"Well, don't talk bad when this child, Isatu is around. We don't know for sure."

"Exactly," emphasised Femi. "Well if you don't know - don't accept, not so. There is no way I would allow any son of mine to bring that kind of *fleke-fleke* girl into my family without knowing her family background.

"Femi, hence you have no children, you don't know what you would be willing to put up with. When you have wanted so lo-o-o-ng for a grandchild, and it is from your eldest and only son, I'm telling you, there are strange things you will do."

She paused.

"It's like being in love. You do foolish things - not as though you would know about that either. But me!! Hmm! No sah! I wouldn't allow it. Umm, Umm."

She clicked her tongue as she spoke and shook her head with strong disapproval as the rhythm and pace of her fleshy arm turned the meat.

Femi gave Omo a look with eyes that said, "You see me here, I could so easily pull out your tongue." She restrained her hand to a pronounced picking of the rice instead, and gave unusually avid concentration to flicking broken bits of the long grain rice out of her nails as she did so.

"I am sure that Mama now would not put up with it if she knew that she may have grandchildren from the others. But those girls are still there. Do you know that Rasheda is already way into her 30's?"

At this, Isatu eagerly made a contribution in defence of her cousin.

"But Auntie, Rasheda and myself, I'm sure we are about the same age. And I'm only 28."

"E-xactly!"

"Not married, no children. Just a ca-reer Whats a career? She'd better be careful because now, this country starts taking out women's insides at her age. Maybe that's what she wants so she no longer has to pretend about wanting a man and having children."

"What do you mean?" Isatu said, slightly taken aback but still unwilling to pry.

"What she means is that Rasheda is one of these lesbo's."

"Femi!" Omo screeched. "Not in front of Isatu now!"

"What! So you haven't instructed your daughter on the goings on in this country? That women play with women and it's called normality. You haven't told her? Be quick Omo before she finds out for herself."

"Are you suggesting that my daughter," the flick of the spoon out of the pot splattered the kitchen with tiny flecks of spicy oil as she swung round to lash Femi with her tongue, making Femi wish that she had jumped from her seat and grabbed it.

"I'm not say-ying a-ny-thing, Omo. Take it easy-eh! All I'm saying is this. This is a different life, a different culture and you know our children can follow any damn thing in this country. We can only keep Africa in our homes. It stops at the doorstep. Tek time. That's all I'm saying. Tek T-i-me."

"Oh, okay. Don't make me sweat. Isatu, haven't you finished chopping those onions yet? Good. Now open the tins of to-ma-tis, the tomato paste - we are slowing down oh!" She sang out the last sentence.

"All this jabba-jabba is slowing us down."

"Here. I've finished the rice. What else is there to do? Where is Mama?" asked Femi.

"She left me in charge," Omo ballooned with self importance.

"You know she has much to sort out, to make sure everything is on time. Can you make the rice bread? The ground rice is there, on top of the fridge. The bananas are soft enough, they won't take long to mash. Let's not be late now."

"Does it matter. The parents are likely to arrive late anyway."

"How can you be so pessimistic, Femi."

"I'm not. I'm just stating a possibility."

"Hmm. Don't you think Mama has enough problems of her own without you wishing her the worst? She has to cope with this jackass son, who gives his mother a grandchild, who may not even be part of the family, a daughter who doesn't like men. And another one who flits here and there . . . no-one knows where she is. What she does or even who she does it with!" Her voice ended on a high note with spoon in hand, other hand on hip. "So, can't you be just a bit more helpful and respectful? Honestly children, eh. They can kill you, the way they carry on! If they were mine! The problem is," she stopped cooking and turned round to face them again. "Its discipline." She spat the words out. "They are not disciplined. Mama was too easy on them. She wanted to give them the best of western education and all they took on was the worst western manners and she let them carry on. She should have beat them. Solidly. And look at Brima Junior. He didn't pick up any education at all. What kind of father will he be - even if the childs is his, as we say. Poor child. Look at the mother eh! Did you know she already has two other children by two different fathers? She doesn't want to work that's what it is. These Jamaican girls, they're all the same. What kind of daughter-in-law is that ? And you know," she turned and dropped her jaw, when she first met Mama, she called her by her first name - her first name! Can you imagine. I don't even know myself what it is. Manners. The child has no manners. What do you expect being brought up with no father? I suppose we should just give thanks to God that she is . . ."

As she muttered these words, she took her first finger, held out her arm and rubbed her skin with it then slapped her hips and raised her head to the ceiling in praise of God. Then she turned back to the steaming pot.

Femi sat, nonchalant, chewing on kola. She was preparing. She rolled the bits of kola round in her mouth, then spat them out in a precise neat mound onto the pile of onion skins and other vegetable peelings in the Marks and Spencer carrier bag serving as a bin.

"Only half."

"Only what?"

"I said," she drawled, "half."

"Half of what?"

"The other half is Irish."

"You are kidding me." She shook her head.

"I-mi-grant Ireesh. From Liverpool."

"What this one?"

"Noooo. Not this one. The youngest ones own man. I saw them together one eve' nin as I was on my way home. Kissing- kissing on the top of the bus. She didn't even notice me. If she had, she probably wouldn't even have known I was her auntie, anyway. So little does she see of the family."

"Does Mama know?"

"How would I know. And even is she does, you think she would tell us. Is that something you want to spread around in the family?"

"How do you know he was - half - what? Don't talk behind the woman's family like this. Femi - it's not nice. How do you know he is half Irish?"

"They were talking about going back home for Christmas. And does her family come from Dublin?" She looked at Omo sarcastically.

"Eh, Papa God!" Auntie Omo balanced one arm on her torso and pulled her lip with the other.

"Children can kill you. This poor woman is suffering. Half Irish not even half English. I can't believe it. Which might have been a bit better you know. There is no way on this earth I would suffer that. I would beat her until she came back to her senses. Mama can't control these children of hers. Its because they were all born here and now they have white-white ways. No respect for family. No respect for tradition. They've never even been back home you know. That's why. If they had been back, left there for a good few years, then I'm sure, these kind of things wouldn't happen.

That's why it is only now I'm allowing Isatu to come here, you know. Let her have the discipline back home first. Now she knows where her family is from, none of this jump up, jump around business. Look, she is here in the kitchen with us for the cook, where are mama's ___"

She stopped in mid flow. Mama came bustling in. A small woman, agile with sharp darting eyes, slightly prominent that reminded one of a chameleon, taking everything in with one glance. Her hands darted too. Within seconds it seemed, she had swished the pots on the stove, grabbed a handful of rice to check that it was well picked and settled her presence on the kitchen.

"All's well," she said in a minute voice.

"Yes ma," Auntie Omo said

"Don't cook the meat thoroughly Omo, before adding the onions."

"Oh, of course not, ma."

Omo quickly ushered Isatu over with those that were finely chopped and swooped them off the chopping board and into the pot.

"And I thought that we could cook the couscous as well, you know for those who don't want jollof rice - is that okay? Mama stated rather than asked.

"No problem, mama. We'll do that right now. Femi?" She diverted her energies over to her as if they had only been talking food and Femi raised herself slowly from the chair and into action.

"Mama, don't worry we are taking care of everything from this side. How is the other house doing."

"They'll soon be here with the rest of the food."

"Good. Then we're all set," Omo said.

"The *comojade* will go well, ma. We're all happy for you, you know."

"Bless you, bless you", ma said softly. "I don't know what I would have done without your help and support. I now that you are family but you have done too much, too much Omo. *Kushe - ya.*"

"Well, you now we are all family. It's to be expected. You didn't think we would rally round and help for this great family occasion?" Omo opened her eyes big-big one.

"Well," mama said. "Considering the circumstances, you never know who of our family will be there."

"We are always here for you, you know that."

"You're lucky you have Isatu, my own two girls, are nowhere to be seen. You did the right thing Omo, bringing over Isatu when she had sense enough to know and understand the right thing. Oh well." She shrugged her shoulders and whirled out.

Isatu took that as her cue to leave. Knowing her mother, now swollen with self importance about her obedient daughter it would be easy for her to slip out.

"Ma, do you mind if I go now? I have studies to do."

Her mother waved her on, in fact pleased, so that she could dig Femi for more chitta-chatta, which she felt she couldn't do in quite the same way whilst Isatu was there.

"Well tell me now," she leaned over eagerly before Isatu had barely closed the door behind her.

As she reached the front door, Isatu quickly looked around, opened the broom cupboard and deftly snatched a small bag hanging
there. In one fluid movement as though rehearsed several times over, Isatu opened the door of her aunts house, stepped carefully over the doorstep in the snow, closed it behind her and went running down the path, out the gate, across the road and up the side road to the small blue car waiting for her.

Listening to that conversation between her mother and Aunt Femi, had convinced her. There would be no good in explaining the way her stomach filled with butterflies and her body prickled with heat, each time she leant over the freckled face of her lover. She smiled and slipped her hand over her smooth creamy breast.

Kadija Sesay

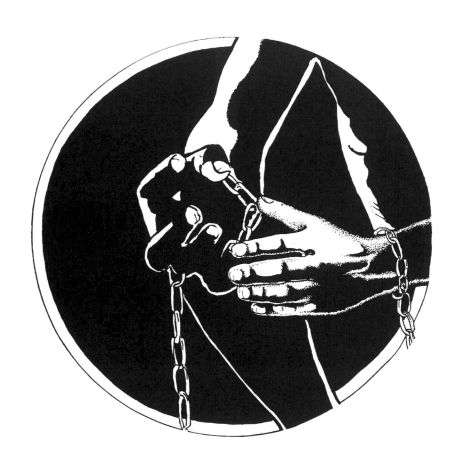

A NAMING POEM

When I raise my fist in this salute
I am Jesse Owen jumping past Hitler's
Aryan Supermen.

When I raise my fist in this salute, Malcolm
looks up from his books and smiles,
Mandela looks from his Robben Island cell
and nods, Garvey tips his brocaded hat, Marley blows
ganja my way, Rosa Parks holds tighter
onto her seat on that bus.

When I raise my fist in this salute
I am Fidel Castro turning back the Yankees,
I am Bogle L'Ouverture kicking colonial ass,
I am Kwame Nkrumah starting the African Revolution.

When I raise my fist in this salute
I see the whites of my oppressor's eyes curdle,
I see every black woman, every black man, every black
child
still waiting for justice - I see them all
raise their fist too. And I realise
together we are strong
together we'll win through.
This fist I raise
I raise for you.

Pete Kalu

61

TOWER BLOCKING

Like some index fingured insult
on some futureless horizon,
From plantations to tower block estates
pre-fab buildings for pre-fab lives,
No easy life on hell's sixteen levels,
as rudeboys revel in a sad situation
ghetto-rebel education
with diplomas in death,
each horror story set
on top the other,
victims in a junk pile of no-hope
searching for lost dreams in coke
to sedate the day.
Pre-teens buy pampers baby-dry,
Boom bye-bye fantasies seduce,
cause when you trapped in a sky-cell
black life and media myths merge..
Skyscraping tombstone community
where nobody really lives,
cause nobody gives a damn.
Piss stench burn de smell from noses,
hallway shit stains my mental
grafitti walls sent all my thoughts
hurtling in a haze of colour.
Pushers gaze my kids
and erase my smile
as yuh remember
your children home alone
yuh can't afford a sitter
flipping burgers in McSlavery.
Faces etched in pain
people go insane as
life becomes a misery.
Little fellas kicking corridor goals
wid green gardens on dey mind
16 floors too far for mama eyes...
Tower blocking hopes
Tower blocking dreams
Man ah have to get out of here!
Yuh don't want to stay
Yuh can't afford to leave
man ah have to get out of here!
It too hard
living in a cell block sober!
Man ah have to get out of here!

**Roger
Robinson**

62

STRANGE FRUIT

Strange fruit
hanging from the tree,
castrated for all to see,
that he was the epitomy
of Klu Klux Klan brutality.

Strange fruit
dangling from the tree
covered in fresh blood,
around that anatomy
the white man's warped mentality
that led him to believe
the black man's sexual potency
was a threat to white society.

Strange fruit
swaying gently with the summer breeze
and the flies, birds and bees
are at ease,
feasting at all they can see,
under the big oak tree.

Strange fruit
lifeless from the tree,
a monument of inhumanity,
a reminder of the white man's barbarity,
despite his claims to supremacy.

Ama Biney

INCIDENTS AT 3a.m.

In the soft lampness
of the room
You blow bubbles and snore
dreams of jungles
corporate meetings
falling ravished
fears and peppermint

Somewhere
a woman reaches for
her shoes
subconsciously
practices
her Kegel exercises*
delivers up a short
prayer
for infertility.

Leone Ross
*Exercises for the internal pelvic floor muscles.

R u m - a n - C o k e

Norma Browne got up early, cried a bit, stared at her hand and muttered to herself with a reluctant, bitter conviction, 'Was a waste. A waste!'

Nobody heard her except perhaps the boy; but even if he had, he would not remember much, come daylight.

Come daylight, he would lurch out of the house, hungry, ill and angry, his body starved of something that she or no food on earth could satisfy. He would be away a couple of hours or maybe the whole day, and then he would return to lay below the house, the turbulence gone - miraculously - except in the working of his eyes. He would not be able to look at her, not until the shivering started again - very late in the evening and he began, once more, to hit her.

She got up early because a thought had nudged her out of sleep, an idea - appallingly straightforward - which, with the coming daylight became a set, focused resolve.

She waited until he left then dressed herself clumsily but quickly in the light blue dress that, fifteen years ago, she'd bought for his Christening and which ten years later, she also wore to take him to that special school in Saint George's. He was a beautiful boy then, clear-eyed and quick, his little body full of purpose. 'Remarkably intelligent' was what the teachers said; and to prove they were not lying, they'd written it on a pretty piece of parchment paper, framed it and handed it to her.

Not like now, she thought. Not like now at all - because what she used to feel then went way past pride. And if, in those days, she felt embarrassed or even terrified, it was only because she could hardly believe that someone like her could be so blessed.

With the same awkward haste, Norma Browne knelt and reached beneath the iron bed. She dragged out what looked like a pillow and emptied its contents on the floor. Several objects rolled out of the wads of fabric she would never use for anything but kept anyway 'just in case': a couple of heavy silver bracelets, a ring of pure Guyana gold, an old passport with a very clear photo of a man that looked exactly like her son and a small blue book on which The Co-operative Bank was printed in large letters.

She took the little book, stuffed it down her bosom and went to the main road to wait for the only bus that travelled twenty miles, twice a day, to and from Saint George's.

It was evening when she returned. The migrating birds that spent the November and December months in the swamp half a mile away, were already dropping like black rain out of an inflamed sky and settling on the mangroves.

She went straight to the bedroom to replace the book and leave a small but heavy parcel beneath the bed. Then she began to look for things to do. She would have gone to the garden at the top of the hill above the village, but she'd already sown more corn and peas than she had ever sown before, she'd weeded the sweet potatoes, reinforced the mud rows with wattle and bamboo, trimmed the bananas and cleared the stones which, every year, appeared miraculously in the soil. She'd put new campèche pillars under the house, added a kitchen and re-laid the yard with stones she'd gathered from the roadside. Anything that hard work could possibly achieve to ease her days, she'd already done. And if it were possible to undo it all and start again she would gladly do so, because hard work saved her from remembering - even though she'd learnt that not remembering was not the same as forgetting. Not remembering was holding back the shame, or redirecting it the way the drains she dug during the Rainy Season turned excess water away from her garden.

She saw him coming and she got up, studying his face, his walk, the set of his mouth. It was always important that she catch his mood, because it determined how her day went, although when he returned he was never violent. He would have gone over to Teestone's house next door or to some friend of his and pumped his veins with a needleful of that milky stuff which did such dreadful things to him.

The milky stuff - she did not understand it: she thought she had already seen or imagined every awful thing there was, but nothing in her life had prepared for what they called 'de niceness': niceness, because of the way it made them feel, they said; niceness that had sucked the life out of her child and replaced it with another sort of existence - an animated deadness that had reduced her to nothing in his eyes.

Before the deadness was the hunger. He was hungry all the time and she fed him more and more while he seemed to grow thinner by the hour. He'd also become secretive and had lost the quiet temper he was born with. When the shivering started and there was nothing she could do for him, he would scream at her and hit her.

And sometimes she wondered which was worse: his torment or her own shame before the village. Once she caught him doing it to himself panic-ridden and slobbering until he'd fed the beast inside his veins.

For this - for this especially - she did not blame him because he was her child and once, she had known him differently. True, she'd seen him do a few things, some of which violated her sense of decency - like the time she caught him with his cousin - younger than him by two years on her bed and she'd almost killed him - but apart from that Daniel was a perfect boy.

******

68

She would never know how it started, or what it was she did or did not do, or give him, that made him need 'de niceness' which consumed him so completely. But now, she knew who gave it to her boy and that was partly why she went to town. Nobody had told her; they'd only confirmed the truth for her.

It was that gold chain she bought him as a present that made her know. He'd asked for it before he did the exams, set himself his own condition, told her if he got an 'A' for all of them, she should buy him a gold chain with his name written on it. And of course she'd sent her macmère Grace, to Saint George's to get it straight away. Then she hid it in her pillow case and waited. And when he came home one day and told her that he'd got all his 'A's, she went straight to the bedroom and brought it out. That amazed him - not the chain but the fact that she believed he would get the 'A's just because he said so.

So when she saw that gold chain around Teestone's neck it suddenly made sense. Everything made sense: the house Teestone was improving, the way the children flocked him, the girls warring amongst themselves for his attention.

And from then, over the months, she'd studied him. Teddy Stonewall - that boy! That boy who'd never seen a classroom in all his life, who'd never lifted a finger for his mother; who'd grown up by the roadside near the rumshop watching the world slip past; that boy who, having worked for nothing, wanted everything. And over the past months she saw the way it all came to him: the pretty clothes; the new, red Suzuki bike, other people's children. Then the large cars with darkened windows began to arrive from Saint George's.

She would watch them come and go till well past midnight or till the beasts awakened in Daniel's veins and she had to turn to him.

At first her interest in Teestone was incidental - no more than the curiosity of an adult in the goings-on of the young. That was in the early days when she knew nothing of the powder; had seen Daniel suck it up his nostrils a couple of times and believed him when he told her it was no different from a sweet, a new something to tantalise the young; and she thought that it would pass like those little obsessions her boy developed from time to time and then relinquished for his books. Besides, it didn't use to make him ill and he hadn't begun to hit her.

Why she didn't think of going to see Teestone sooner amazed her. It was as if the idea had been ripening inside her and now that it had done so, she couldn't wait to meet the young man whom a powder had made so powerful, the whole world was frightened to displease him.

The rest of the day burnt itself out rapidly. Its charred remains hung indecisively over the houses of the village. Her boy had begun to stir in sleep.

With a series of rapid, nervous movements she straightened her dress, left her house and crossed over to Teestone's yard.

He came out when she called, his body blocking the doorway completely. She had to look up to examine his face against the darkness of the door-mouth. This she did quickly before bringing her head back down. Now she watched him with her eyes upturned.

"What you want, Miss Lady."

"I want to come in," she said.

"Come in where!" He glared down at her. "Come inside o my house! What you want in my house!"

"Is someting," she lowered her voice and her eyes, afraid that he would not let her in. "Is someting I want to buy. I kin pay," she added hastily.

"I tell you I sellin anyting? What you waan to buy!" He was still fuming but his voice, like hers, was lowered.

"I waan some niceness," she said flatly and lifted her eyes at him. He paused a moment, shifted his body and she slipped under his arm. Teestone pulled the door behind him.

Now that the door was closed, he was suddenly transformed, almost like another person. Relaxed, smiling, he drew a wooden stool from under the mahogany table in the middle of the room and placed it before her. Carefully, Norma Browne lowered herself.

Teestone grinned at her unease. "Miss Norma what you say you want?"

"I jus waan some - some of dat ting dat make my son, make my son so - happy." She halted on the last word, made it sound like the most frightful thing on earth. But she managed a smile and that put Teestone at ease. He seated himself a few feet in front of her. He smiled wider and she noticed the gold tooth. She did not remember him having a gold tooth. He had bad teeth anyway, the sort that prised his lips apart, permanently.

The shirt, she also noticed, was of a soft material that dropped as if it were liquid; made, no doubt, from one of those fabulous materials she had seen in pictures in Grace's magazines, and in the large stores through whose wide glass windows you feasted your eyes, but never entered because the light-skinned woman at the counter and the way everything was laid out just told you that you! you'd better not come in.

"What you offerin," he whispered, and for a moment she did not understand him. "What you have," he repeated.

She allowed her eyes to wander around the room before easing her fingers down her bosom and pulling out an old handkerchief. It was rolled into a knot. The thin hands held it curiously, the curl of the fingers, accentuating their frailty. There was a scar at the back of the left, as if she had been burnt there, very badly, once. The fingers un-knotted the bit of cloth to reveal a ball of crumpled notes.

"A thousan dollars," she said and dropped it on the table. It was all she had. The gesture said so, that and her trembling hands. She was never likely to have that much again, for it had taken a lot from her to get it. One thousand dollars that would have gone to her boy along with the house and the piece of land that had been in the family for as long as anyone could remember.

Teestone did not reach for the money, in fact he looked at her as if he were seeing her for the first time - a sudden probing interest, and something like suspicion because she was offering all of it to him. But she was an old woman, in trouble and confused because her son was in trouble and confused. Because, now, her son belonged to him. His eyes barely concealed his hostility. The stupid kind. The kind he despised most: those women who would do anything to please their sons, who never saw the sky because, all their lives, they were too busy looking down, digging and scratching the earth; demeaning and denying themselves - for what? It always puzzled him how people like that ever came by money. A thousand dollars! And it was already his. All of it. It had always been his! For, if she had not given it to him herself, her son would have, eventually, bit by bit. They were all coming now, these old women. When their children could no longer get to him on their own, they were the ones who came and begged for them. Norma Browne was not the first, and she would not be the last. And the best part was, these days he did not have to do a thing. These days money, wherever it was, made its way to him.

"Hold on," he told her, opened the door behind him and disappeared into his bedroom.

Slowly, her eyes travelled around the room.

In the centre of a tiny table in the corner, there was a framed picture of Teestone, his mother, and the man his mother had lived with but who, she knew without a doubt, wasn't his father at all - although she'd made the man believe he was. To the right of that there was another photo of a child.

Having nothing better to do, Norma Browne examined the picture of the baby sitting on a straw mat staring out at the camera with a child's wide-eyed, open-mouthed, bewilderment. He hadn't grown out of that wide, wet mouth, nor indeed those eyes that seemed smaller than they really were because of the heaviness of the lids. She replaced the picture, cautiously.

He was rebuilding the house his mother had left him, or rather he was replacing the wood with concrete, which meant erecting blocks against the board walls outside. When they were set in cement he would knock the planks out one by one from inside. Now, even before he'd done that, the wet concrete was seeping through the boards, leaving a pale sediment which, when she passed her hand along it, left an ugly trace of powder and tiny bits of wood on her fingers. Electrical wires ran everywhere: along the floorboards, the ceiling and the walls and she realised that the rumours she'd heard were true. Teestone was bringing electricity to his house. Or he was having that man who came in the long, black car on Fridays - that man they called The Blade - make the government do it for him. A couple of large, soft chairs lay upturned in a corner, completely covered with transparent plastic, and to the left of her there was a gaping hole through which she could see the earth below the house. Perhaps they had opened it up, she speculated, because he was replacing the wooden pillars too.

The smell of concrete was everywhere: intrusive, corrosive - as brash as the youths who, wherever she turned, were remaking everything, upsetting everything, undoing everything - the way wood mites secretly hollowed out a house and all the while you did not know that you were surrounded by nothing until a small wind passed one day and blew it down around you, like a stack of rotting leaves.

She was still contemplating this scene of quiet devastation when Teestone came out with a small brown bag - the type the shop sold sugar by the half pound in. He did not place it in her hand but on the mahogany table in front of them. She took it up with a confident gesture and for a moment, in fact for the first time she seemed different, self-possessed.

She opened the bag carefully and clumsily dragged out the small plastic sac that was folded inside it.

"S'not a lot," she said, shocked. "Not a lot for all my money."

Teestone laughed then, laughed till the fat vein at the side of his neck stood out. Fascinated, she watched that neck-vein throb and pulse with laughter.

"S'what you expect? Dis, dis worth more dan it weight in gold, y'know dat? More-dan-it-weight-in-gold."

He spoke the last few words as if they were one, as though he'd rehearsed it till it sounded that way: rhythmic and convincing.

"Ask anybody." Teestone added, emphatically.

"Didn know," she apologised and then she brought it to her nose. She froze, fixing very dark eyes on him. "It s'pose to smell like dat? Like, uh, baby powder?" She queried, balling her fist around the packet. She was looking at him closely but he did not notice this. What he saw was a small woman, old before her time, almost doubled over with hard work with a nervous hand and a frightened voice, trying to get some stuff off him. His contempt had denied him of the details, and so he had no sense of her: the very, very steady eyes, the tight-set mouth that had lost or given up the habit of laughter, a generous forehead, partly covered by an old head wrap and a tendency to follow his every movement.

So her question took him completely by surprise. The slight narrowing of his eyes and the way he tried to close his mouth without really managing it, confirmed her suspicion.

"It not s'pose to smell o baby powder," she told him quietly, a new hardness in her voice.

Is so it smell, he was about to tell her, and ask her what de hell she know 'bout niceness, anyway, but her directness stopped him - that and her very steady gaze. He snatched the packet off the table and went back inside the bedroom. This time he returned sooner, dropped the packet on the table and sat back heavily.

Norma took the packet from the table, shook it, then passed it under her nose. She could see by his expression that he wanted her to leave. He was tired, or perhaps, now that his business with her was over, he wanted to get rid of her. But she was not finished with him yet.

She wanted to know how she should prepare the stuff and he showed her. Her hands shook when she took the needle to examine the thin, evil thread of metal that slipped so easily into flesh. The first time she saw her boy use it, it had made her sick. He had taken it standing and had fallen straight back against the floorboards, his body rigid, like a tree deprived suddenly of its roots, doing nothing to break the fall. He'd cut his head badly, and did not even know it, just laid there with that smile, that awful inner peace, while she turned him over and tended to his wound.

In her hand the metal shone like an amber thread of light against the lamp.

"All ov it is fo de boy?" Asked Teestone, showing her his tooth.

Some was fo her son, she answered, and well, she was goin to use de rest. Was de niceness nicer if she used all of it in one go?

No, he told her, and the gold tooth glimmered in the light. If she used more than he just showed her - at that he pulled out a packet of razor blades, extracted one, opened the packet he'd handed her and separated a small portion, working it with the same care that she used to mix medicine for her boy's illness when he was a child. If she ever used more than that, he pointed at the tiny heap he'd separated, it would kill her.

"Too much niceness does kill. Y'unnerstan?" He laughed at his own joke, lit a cigarette and leaned back against the chair. That too was new, the long cigarettes with the bit of silver at the end; in fact everything about Teestone was new, even his face. There was not the redness in the eyes, the dreadful tiredness that went deeper than age, the loosening of something precious and essential in the face, the damp surrender of the skin - once smooth and dark and beautiful with youth - to that terrible hunger that made her son strike out at her. Teestone looked fresh and happy and as alert as a cat. Money had made him handsome.

Suddenly she felt relaxed. "Could ha been a nice house," she said, looking around the room, smiling the smallest of smiles, happier now than she had been for the past twelve months, from the time she discovered that her son was stuffing his veins with poison.

It was perhaps out of that odd sense of abeyance that she reached out suddenly and fixed Teestone's collar: or, she might have been prodded by a desire to get an idea of what that shiny material really felt like. Her fingers brushed the side of his neck, touching the laughing vein which made him recoil with a violence she thought entirely undue.

She pretended not to notice his outrage, got up slowly and shuffled towards the door. There, she stopped and turned back to Teestone.

"He lef school last year," she told him with a quiet, neutral look. "My Dan jus come an tell me dat he leavin school, and I say, 'you can't: you can't becoz you always tell me dat you want to see de world, dat you'll make me proud and build a nicer house for us when you become someting. You say you see how hard it is fo me. How much I does do fo you and how much I'll always do fo you.' An he laugh, like he woz laughing at someting he know inside hi head, he say he don't need to go no way no more to see de world, becoz he could see it from right dere where he lie down whole day on hi back below my house. He tell me what he see sometimes and I can't make no sense of it. Coz I can't see inside mih lil boy head. I can't make no sense o people walkin over precipice an dem not dyin, o animal dat talk an laugh with you inside you head. I can't. But he say he see dem and it make im happy. But is when de niceness get bad," she added softly, apologetically, "and I can't do nothing and I just hear im bawl an bawl an bawl, an he start hittin me, dat I does - well I does jus tek it. Y'know sometimes he hit me - my son? Hit me like he father used to?"

Her voice had dropped to a whisper and it was thick and dark and gentle, and tinged with a terrible sadness. "I let im - I let im till he get tired an fall asleep. He don sleep no more like he used ter. Is like someting in hi sleep, in hi dreamin beatin im up same like he do wit me. All de time. Dat's why - dat's why I does..."

Teestone got up suddenly.

"You get what you want, Miss Lady. Go!"

He'd already pushed open the door for her.

Norma Browne walked out into a close, choked night that had settled on the village like a blanket and beyond which nothing - not even the screaming of those birds in the swamp - seemed to escape.

There were some girls outside, a few of them not more than fourteen, their precocious eyes fixing her incredulously, and then an instant later turning to the doorway with that still and hungry gaze she'd seen so often in her son during the quiet times when the shivering stopped and she'd force fed him or tried to. She knew all of them - some she'd even delivered before her hand went funny: or, as children, she'd kept them for their mothers when they went off to Saint George's for medicine or some necessary thing that their hillside gardens or the sea could not provide.

At their age, she thought, life was supposed to be kinder - as it had been, even for her - an enormous promise which never lasted long, but was part of growing up. It belonged to that age. Was part of what kept you going for the rest of your life. And you should not miss it.

She decided not to go home. Her boy would be there now beneath the house laid out on his back sleeping or talking to himself. He would remain there until she came and brought him in. Or if she did not feel like it, she would leave him there until he was conscious again - perhaps some time close to morning - when he would beat her door until she let him in. Tonight he would not touch her because she had what it took to quiet him.

And that was another thing: he would not beg anymore, not offer Teestone anything - anything at all for the relief of a needle. Once she saw him beg and it had shamed her. Saw him do it yesterday and it had shamed her even more because Teestone's refusal had brought him raging to her yard.

She took the track that ran off from the main road, which used to take him to the school he'd won the scholarship for in Saint George's.

It was a long, hard walk because the rains from the weeks before had made a drain of the mud track. The pebbles slipped under her feet and she was forced to steady her progress by grabbing at the bushes on the side. Ordinarily, she would have taken a bottle torch but that was only when she planned a visit; tonight, the parcel held firmly in her hand, it had suddenly seemed like common sense that she should visit Grace. It was Grace who first told her about Daniel: how on mornings when he left for school he got off the bus a mile away, and doubled back to feed his veins all day on Teestone's powder. It was Grace who - without moving from her house had found out where it came from and the nickname of the government man that visited Teestone every Friday night.

Grace was the only one to whom she spoke these days: Grace, with the cat's eyes who used to have the gentlest of husbands; whose five daughters had all gone away and sent her money every month, from England, America and Canada; who'd offered to buy her son's uniform as a lil present for winning the scholarship. Grace who always got much more than she deserved from life.

The back of her hand was scratching her - the deep, insistent scratch that she could not reach because it was beneath the skin. Years ago, her left hand did not scratch that way, nor was there the white scar at the back of it where the skin had been cut away and then healed very badly. And it did not curl itself up as it did now. Many people, those who did not remember or rather those that forgot too easily, thought she had been born that way but Grace remembered that she wasn't. Grace remembered everything.

Grace's place was neat and small and full of colour. There were large blood-red hibiscus on her curtains and the enamelled bowls and cups, and the glasses in the cabinet had bouquets of flowers patterned all over them. Even her dress was a flower garden. God had given her eyes that shone like bits of coloured glass which, depending on her mood, were exactly like a cat's. Her friend burned three kerosene lamps instead of one. Big lamps - the ones marked Home Sweet Home in white on the shade - that they sold for ten dollars at Everybody's store in Saint George's and whose combined brightness gave an amazing, shadowless quality to the room.

Grace settled her down and retreated to the kitchen. She returned with a bowl of soup and handed it to Norma who looked hesitantly up at her.

"Eat!" she grunted.

"I done eat arready."

"Den eat again. When trouble eatin people, people have to eat back! So take de food an eat!"

The sweet smell of stewed peas and provision and salt meat almost made her faint. She hadn't eaten and Grace knew that she was lying. These days, she'd lost her appetite for everything. Most times she forgot to eat at all. She placed the packet on the table and took up the bowl.

Grace looked at the brown bag frankly - a question in her eyes.

"How's de boy," she mumbled, still staring at the paper bag.

"Cost me everything. All dat was left - a thousand dollars," Norma said it as if the 'everything' was more important than the money.

"What cost what!" asked Grace.

"Dat." Norma nudged the bag with the handle of the spoon.

Grace reached for it and opened it. The powder was on her fingers when she withdrew her hand. It could have been the effect of the lamplight on her silver bracelets but her hand seemed to tremble. The woman's face went dead. "A thousand dollars! Fo-"

"Dat," Norma Browne said, herself quietly appalled. "De rest of de money. What left. I draw it out today."

"Jeezas Christ - you, you buy dat poison fo you boy! You mad!"

Norma Browne continued eating, but she looked up and exposed her face to Grace: a very dark woman, always alert - the kind of intelligence another woman noticed right away. She used to be beautiful, and could still be when she laughed, but laughter like so many other things had died when the trouble with her son began.

"You think so?" She muttered, with complete unconcern. And that left a chill in Grace's stomach.

"Whey he is?" Grace asked.

"Below de house. Sleepin." Norma swallowed. "He tired."

"Still - erm - hittin you?" Grace went completely still.

Norma stopped short, the bit of meat held contemplatively between her thumb and index. She nodded.

"Firs de father and den de son. God bless me I don have no boy chile. But I wish, I wish I had a boy to raise hi hand and touch me! Jeezan bread, I wish dat if.." she stopped breathless, the eyes flaming in the lamplight, made inarticulate by the thought of what she would do any boy child, if! "God forgive me but I'll make dat sonuvabitch wish he never born."

Norma smiled, "Dat's de problem. You don see? If he's a son ova bitch, dat mean I'z de bitch dat make dis son. I don wish he never born but sometimes - sometimes I wish he don live no mo - to ease, to ease im up a bit." She looked up apologetically.

Grace grunted irritably. "You - you not goin ter let im continue!"

"Nuh." Norma licked her fingers. "Nuh, I goin stop im. Tonight."

The certitude in her voice made Grace lean closer. "You goin ter.. Jeezas, gyul. Jeezas!

"I not goin ter, y'know - but like I say, I think of it sometimes - sometimes, all de time, for a whole day, I think of it. If y'all hear im bawlin, not to bother. Tell everybody not to bother." Something in her tone turned Grace's eyes to Norma's hand, the one that lay curled up like a bird's claw in her lap.

That hand alone was reason enough for everyone to bother. What kind of woman would place her hand between the cogs of a machine so that she could get the insurance money to send her boy off to a high-class school in Saint George's. Inside a sawmill besides! And if she could do that to herself for him, what on God's earth wouldn't she do to make her sacrifice worthwhile?

"Go easy," muttered Grace, taking up the bowl of unfinished food and heading for the kitchen. It was both a warning and a farewell and sensing this, Norma got up.

"If you hear him - " she started.

"Uh-huh," Grace answered - a little too brusquely perhaps - without turning round. "Rum-an-coke is what dey call it." She called out from the kitchen. "Dey take dat ting and drink down rum right after. Dat's what make dem mad an beat up deir own flesh-an-blood so bad."

"Ah know." Norma curled her hand around the packet. All of a sudden the room felt too bright for her, she lifted her bad hand above her eyes as if to shade them from the sun. She paused briefly at the doorway, made as if to say something then changed her mind before slipping out into the night.

Back home, she helped the boy from under the house and led him to the bedroom. He was quiet and aware of her but she knew that soon he would be shivering. She lit the lamp, undressed him and bathed him like she used to, the way she thought she'd forgotten. And then she went back to the kitchen.

There, she carved out a portion of the stuff exactly as she'd seen Teestone do. She knew where he kept his needle, knew what she had to do.

She went in, laid the small bag down beside the door. He'd already begun to shiver.

"C'mon Bumpsy, take this fo mammy," she said, speaking to him exactly as she would a baby; and he seemed, from somewhere deep inside, to recognise that tone; began curling his shirt ends between his fingers like he used to when he was a child, while he looked at her with a tired, helpless uncertainty.

"S'for you, tek it from Mammy," she urged - the voice soft and sweet and sad and tearful and angry and wretched at the same time.

He took the needle and she watched him unflinching, while he served himself, so hungry for the ease it offered he was almost sobbing. And then while he recovered and swooned and laughed and swam and floated away from her, she reached below the bed, opened the bag and took out the length of chain and the padlocks she had bought in Saint George's. Still cooing her mummy-talk, Norma Browne fastened her son against the bed.

If you hear im bawlin, she'd told Grace - who would, come morning, pass the message on to everyone - If you hear im bawlin, tell everybody not to bother. And she knows the bawling would begin soon, or some time in the morning, or perhaps the next day, and it would go on for a long time, perhaps forever.

Back in the kitchen she mixed most of what remained of the powder in the paper bag. Finished, she leaned out of her window and observed the precocious girls, the motorbikes, the occupants of the occasional car sneaking back and forth between the road and Teestone's house.

She knows that soon the traffic would subside, the lamps go out and the whole world come to a pause while Teestone sleeps.

It is a warm, tense night - lonely too because there is nobody to talk to and the sound of the wind, and the great, starless emptiness above her makes her think of futile distances, of the irreconcilable vastness of the world, her own smallness, and the place she feels she no longer has in it. Becoz a time does reach, she thinks, when a woman only hope fo what come after she: she chil'ren and de chil'ren dat will come from dem - that would pass on and on and on, if not her name, then her blood and perhaps a memory of her; an acknowledgement that they are alive only because she existed, once. Dat, dat's what does mek life worth someting.

Her hand is scratching her again and she thinks that perhaps it will rain. Her hand always scratches before it rains. She is slightly anxious. A low wind stirs the air, shakes the trees above the houses and leaves a smell of cinnamon, swamp and charcoal over the village. As if this were a signal, she straightens up, steps out into the night. Full height, she is much taller than most people have seen her, and she has lost her shuffle as she walks across the yard. She is as soundless as the shadows that moved throughout the early night to and from Teestone's house, and just as silent when she climbs his steps.

She remembers the hole in the living room and avoids it. She carries a very clear picture in her head of the house and everything in it.

The lamp is lit in his bedroom and he is asleep, rolled over on one side and snoring softly. He is naked. One of the girls lies curled up in front of him, naked also, the young hips turned inwards, giving her a curious air of innocence. Sleep has also stripped away what remains of the womanishness she wears by day, almost like another garment, and has made of her a girl again.

She kneels beside Teestone and he stirs, perhaps sensing her in sleep.

The jab wakes him. He erupts out of sleep, his hand clutching that laughing vein at the side of his neck, but she is strong and she keeps him and the needle there until she empties it of her thousand dollars worth of niceness. Eyes wide, Teestone stares at her. His fist closes on her wrist. It is the bad hand that he is crushing and it hurts. But she smiles that dark and beautiful and alluring smile, something wonderful to take with him, she seems to say.

He eases back on the pillow releasing her and sighing the longest, most restful of all sighs, his face still incredulous, still profoundly outraged.

The girl has not stirred from sleep, and for that Norma Browne is grateful. She walks out of the house, turns and spits carelessly at the dark before crossing to her yard. Before she goes in she pauses, turns her face up at the sky and sniffs. She could smell the morning

But it is still dark. And the world and the birds down there are very, very quiet.

Jacob Ross

WHAT'S IN A NAME?

My Christian name was Emmanuel
Which I have had since I was born
But then it dawned, why have this name
When I am African and not a Christian
African and not a Christian

This name was a brand of colonisation
Symbol of our slavery
But I was lucky
Because my mother already gave me an African name
Chu-kwun-yere
Chu-kwun-yere
Can you pronounce that?
Chu-kwun-yere

I was talking to a young French woman one day
She said, "I keep seeing you here but I never caught your
name"
I said Chu-kwun-yere
"What's that?"
Chu-kwun-yere, can you pronounce that?
Chu-kwun-yere
She refused point blank to pronounce may name.
As if it was some kind of hocus-pocus
That would point her in a trance
And switch her off-guard
Now,
Some people say, "Hey! That's a mouthful."
But I'm sorry. All I can say is "Bull!"
We've been trained to like European names
But they can be a mouthful
Just the same
Say E-LI-ZA-BETH, E-LI-ZA-BETH

Can you pronounce that? E-LI-ZA-BETH
Say Bar-thol-lo-mew, Bar-thol-lo-mew,
Can you pronounce that? Bar-thol-lo-mew,
So if you're African, take up your African name
If you're Asian, take up your Asian name
And if you're English......
Take any name you like
You name is your link to your ancestry
or the echo of a subservient past

So break the chain
Reclaim your name

Break the chain
Reclaim your name
Break the chain, break the chain, break the chain....

Chukwunyere Kamalu

OMOWALE
(The child has come home)

I

I dreamt the morning rose over dark waters
with the surprise of a tropical dawn,
the transparency of slow moving clouds
to dissolve in a flawless blue sky,
transforming night to a sea of silver's
mild ripples to soothe my inner chaos.
But this sea is howling wailing wild,
rabid fists of water surge, arch, hover mid air
then thrust forwards with the rolling raging
gravitas of an unbridled revenge.
Water drenches the hapless shore, sinking sand,
undercurrents frantically grasping granules
until, washing over itself, the pattern is repeated.
I had heard of a paradise beach, sleepy village
nestled around a fishing bay, children selling
oranges from baskets atop their heads;
of seaside folk who watch the world pass by
and haggle with the tourists.
Yet here at Elmina, facing the fathomless
Atlantic, the sea tells a different tale -
night and day it pounds into my porous senses,
lashes at memory, swamps my idle dreams,
assaults my sleeping mind with fine spray.

II

The guide at the castle is a driven man,
propelled by a passion born of voices
that will not give him rest. He leads me
down massive grey stone and mortar
into a small, dark, musty chamber,
perhaps nine by nine, and windowless.
"Oh Lord!", he moans, arms raised in worship.
Allah, Jesu, Yemanja - Goddess of the Sea!
"Oh Lord!", he intones, his resonant voice
heavy with a groundswell of horror.
"Oh Lord! Keep them alive in us,
let them love, guide and protect us."
My eyes fill quickly with simple tears.
He slams the heavy wooden door shut. Bam!
Pitch black, now airless, in this dungeon
the condemned rebels were left to die.
Three long days it would take, no less.
Now they climb onto my back, tickle
the nape of my neck, pass through me.
I sense the guide, re-incarnate, reading me.
Silence - the sound of those who are not mourned.
Sound - the memory of the forgotten.
Memory - a closed door with no air.

III

Suddenly he swings open the door and light
does not burst in with relief, merely it illuminates
the detail. Desperate markings scratched on stone,
signs - doomed tortured strokes,
a testimony from the dying for the living.
"L'Art des Esclaves - deep and meaningful" - on show
at Elmina Gallery, Ghana. 1000 Cedis. Cheap.
Out in the courtyard, before I can even sigh,
he grabs my mind, pushes it at two cannon balls
sunk in concrete, metal hoops welded on them.
"Naked women chained to balls, on show
for the governor watching from his balcony,
taken via that trap door to his apartment upstairs."
Scenic view, sea breeze creeping through
light, airy, empty rooms. I see you, sir.
There is nowhere to hide anymore. Not behind
battalions, gold, or empires or church.
Yet there are no longer any guilty,
only the dead who keep me awake at night
by the ocean stretching the longest coast,
pouring itself through a hole in my crown,
into my blood, bubbling inside me,
for only the implacable sea is a constant.

IV

In the red-earthed dusty town of Ouidah,
I am shown the home of the iron-eyed
Francisco de Souza, famed trader in human lives,
progenitor of the de Souza dynasty, seeded
in countless countries, who gather to worship he.
His great-grandson, family elder, all limpid
sea-washed eyes and cinnamon skin,
shows me Francisco's bedroom wherein
lies the great man himself,
entombed in the middle of the room.
With watery pride in his smiling eyes
he watches the stunned freeze on my face.
Clearly I am impressed, he nods approvingly,
asks for francs. I say no, my bank is drained.
But the sea can be kind, you know.
It taketh and it giveth. Hallelujah!
It brought my great-grandaddy back from Brazil,
along with the hopes of many emancipado others.
It held them close until they sailed into Lagos,
to a land known only through their forefather's orature.
The sea, at once tomb and messenger, protector,
avenger; always the uncompromising witness.

Bernardine Evaristo

"REVOLUTIONARY" FLIRT

"Revolutionary" flirt,
with your gracious smile
and flirtatious eyes,
attracting sisters
with your wiles and guiles,
I've met your type before,
on the dance floor....
in the days when I used to rave....

Sure,
once upon a time,
you could spin me that line.
But today?
no way!

"Revolutionary" comrade,
clear and 'sound',
going around,
with those seductive glances,
making those advances to an
unsuspecting sister,
who becomes your next victim.

"Revolutionary" flirt,
intent on foreplay,
in almost everything you say,
in suggestive double meanings
which subtly hide your true feelings,
so the sisters get a rough dealing....

"Revolutionary" comrade,
with your well - spun lies and alibis,
I can see why the sisters
have their eyes on you....

But those caught unaware
of your casual affairs,
get broken in two and
abused by you.

Ama Biney

OYINBO
("FOREIGNER" BECAUSE I DO NOT SPEAK MY NATIVE LANGUAGE)

From my mother tongue since birth abducted
Reared in a foreign diction now my own,
slave to the vocabulary of enslavers,
Embarrassment to my own kind
Unkind who scorn my ignorance as arrogance
some vain ambition to be fully westernised.
Victim of misinterpretation, I grin inanely,
playing dumb to derision but too often
wounded by words not even understood.
Private jokes at my expense
closed circles of contempt
exclude me,
I spiral a retreat into my self-defence;
embracing speech I learnt in praise-song poetry
secure that when the time arrives
for those who have ears to hear
there will be no need for translators
biting their own tongues in haste to explicate.
So in this truth I seek respite, licking an ego
resigned to weary questions unreplied;
Questions
as to why I was denied
that portion of my heritage,
forced to adapt and to adopt
this language I have learnt to love
as to why I had no choice
as to
who took away my voice?

Uju Asika

R.A.W.

UNCOOKED
UNCUT
UNCAGED
UNCHAINED
UNCENSORED

Uncooked uncut uncaged unchained uncensored

RAW
rhythm and word
uncooked uncut
uncaged unchained
uncensored

RAW
sucking out the marrow
of a word
from a bone
holding up a mirror
cos RAW is
WAR
fighting for your rights
in an unjust world

I'm not putting on a wig
for this court case
no make-up on my face
I don't want to attract
only to attack
not to cause a fight
but fight a cause
no time to pause
I'm a poet
it's a four-letter word
I could write about the trees
and the flowers
but I write about ROOTS
RAP is my delivery

89

RAW

more bitter than sweet
more twisted than bitter
no throw away words
cos I never drop litter

Poetry is theft
a fact
I'm a word kleptomaniac
I know about the theft act
accuse me of that
if rime's a crime
rap is crap
I don't believe in that
Black people had a history
stolen from them
and we're claiming it
back

They took our languages away
made us pray
to a god with no pigment
a figment of a sick imagination
story of creation flipped
tricked
and no reparation
Ignored the colour of their lord
but when we sang the gospel
it was RAW
Rich though they started out poor
at death's white door
Bessie 'n' Billie
they knew the score

RAW
rhythm and word
uncooked uncut
uncaged unchained
uncensored

RAW
sucking out the marrow
of a word
from a bone
holding up a mirror
cos RAW is
WAR
fighting for your rights
in an unjust world

When we screamed the Black blues
'n' soul when we belted out
belowthebeltjellyrocknrolljazzfunk
wasn't just about sex 'n' junk
If you want a white parallel
look at the politics of punk
When we entertain we edutain
articulate the pain
of our ancestors' ball and chain
rubbing RAW on our psyche
Black culture goes deeper
than X and Nike

RAW
rhythm and word
uncooked uncut
uncaged unchained
uncensored

RAW
sucking out the marrow
of a word
from a bone
holding up a mirror
cos RAW is
WAR
fighting for your rights
in an unjust world

RAW is RAP
taking our languages back
using our own black words
and being heard
It's a political act
to dis the system
with less tune to distract
Those who say too much slang
We can't understand
calling for rap to be banned
ignore the fact
that RAW is RAP
and RAP is RAW
and RAW means WAR
RAW
rhythm and word
uncooked uncut
uncaged unchained
uncensored

RAW
sucking out the marrow
of a word
from a bone
holding up a mirror
cos RAW is
WAR
fighting for your rights
in an unjust world

Patience Agbabi

REAL REVOLUTIONARIES MOVE IN SILENCE

Real Revolutionaries move in silence
Real Revolutionaries move in silence
Real Revolutionaries move in silence

You can say what you want but it don't mean a thing
It's the turning of that thought into action that carries the swing
Nobody is scared of a bees buzz but they are scared of a bees sting
It's not the bark it's the bite
It's not the talk it's the fight

If you spend all your time talking you will never get anything done
It's like you're in the starters block waiting for the starters gun
But if you were blind, deaf and dumb
You wouldn't know, the race had already begun
You wouldn't know you're a dog under a table being fed the masters crumbs
You wouldn't know that your people were homeless and living in the slums
Maybe we would know if we stopped jigging around and showing each
other our gums

In this line of work there is no pay
You will have to think for yourself 24/7 each and every day
You will have to become the attacker and no longer the prey
Knowledge is power and will keep ignorance at bay
We are all actors on stage what part do you play?
You should be one rung higher on the ladder than you were yesterday
Read and listen to what our ancestors had to say
This will help to wipe the plaque from your brain and stop the decay
Keep a picture in your mind of what it is you have to do
And each and every day make sure it's that you pursue
Use your mouth to speak, your ears to hear and your eyes to view
Know the difference between a lie and what is true
Know the difference between who and what has been here since time
in memorial

93

And who and what is brand spanking new
Become a detective hunting, searching for your next vital clue
But!!! stay alert and fresh like the morning dew
Or the next dead revolutionary could be you, or you or you!!!

Real Revolutionaries move in silence
If your are still confused as to what that statement means
I will now throw a little more light on the scene

To be real means to be real to yourself and real to your people
You're not Malcolm X or Harriet Tubman but you can be their equal
Revolution means the movement, the turning of something upside down
Revolution means going against the crowd
Revolutionary means being able to perceive
If you can't go through the wall go over or around

Silence - when you're under pressure will keep you calm
Silence - when there is danger all around will keep you from harm
Listen to your inner voice let that be your alarm

When you think before you talk you are in silence
When you fight before you think now that's meaningless violence
I hope in this poem I have been of some constuctive guidance
As to why
Real Revolutionaries
Must always
move in
Silence.

Adisa

FAÇADE

Meg Owens raised her head from the book she was reading and listened to the shimmering quiet of the library. Her desk was old pine flaxen with age. Graffiti was soaked into its surface and as she shifted she read the words for the hundredth time. Scrawled across the surface was a telephone number. All manner of carnal delights were promised if the reader would dial immediately - for a small fee of course. The generous offer had only one stipulation.

NO AYDS PLEASE

Sometimes she wondered if it was addressed to her. Often the sentence would float unbidden between the paragraphs of Chaucer that she crammed into her brain. Not the phone number and its attendant depravities. Just that final misspelt sentence (no AYDS please no AYDS please no AYDS no RAYDS, no MAYDS, no AYDS please).

Even I can spell that, she thought. There had been so many health campaigns. Outside it was raining and she was alone. Drops streaked silver lines across the sky light window above her, and the clock stood at seventeen minutes to ten. The rust and the rain in the wall had done their thing and now the clock was schizophrenic. Years before it had shone and ticked. Tocked. Clicked. Smooth. So crisp that it set your teeth on edge. Now it went mad on the hour, the clang of its seconds becoming shrieks.

She drew a slow hand through her hair and decided to leave. She could feel the librarian shifting impatiently. His eyes followed her. *Poor girl*, he thought. *Too skinny for my taste.* He went back to sorting books, waiting for her to come to the desk. *Probably read every book in the damned library*, he reflected. His mother had told him that women who read too much were also inclined to excessive masturbation. He had never worked out the connection, but she still phoned him every Thursday and Sunday to tell him just that, her dentures grinding slightly down the clear telephone line. One day he would get up the balls to ask for an explanation. He looked over at Meg once more. She was what his father would call boring. *Except for her blue eyelashes of course*. He sighed and bit his lip.

****

Home was not far. A few blocks away. Tonight, as always, Meg was glad, down Ferde Avenue and around the corner.

But she had to pass Façade first.

That wasn't a problem, she had done it hundreds of times before, hadn't she, she did it every night and now that her finals were coming up - except

Sundays of course, when she stayed at home with Mother, and nothing ever happened, no it didn't...("JESUS! You ain't comin' inside here are ya?")

That was a week ago now - and she supposed that those men - weren't bad - just high spirited, that's all - young men were like that - full of fun (*"Lookit that skinny bitch - no tits, no ass....hey baby, somebody STRETCH you thin?"*)

Mother told her that it was her Christian duty to turn the other cheek. But the boys had not understood the concept, and when she had tried to explain, well, they had been a little indecent and her waist still hurt where they had grabbed her. Two dime sized bruises where their thumbs had sunk into flesh. Mother had seen them but she had said she must have bumped herself, and that was the first lie she had ever told her Mother who never understood her blue eyelashes anyway. The occasional taunt wasn't a problem, (*"You skinny bitch! You ain't worth SHIT"*). It was when they looked and when she looked back. The fact that they were all about the same age as her but they were so different, their lives were so different, and she wanted, wanted to be a little like them, sometimes , just because it was so hard to be her all the time. (*No No No No No, child. Those thoughts are so full of sin I don't know what to do with you!*)

From where she stood at the edge of the parking lot she could see the walls of the club throbbing. They were milling around, breathing in its heartbeat. Cars of every colour and make crowded side by side, eager for old gossip. The best type, redolent with years of detail and ancient morals. The night light gleamed off their shining hides. Deep inside the glow of the headlamps, images of the crowd flickered.

Black leather clung to hips and thighs. Green, silver and red-spike heeled pumps. Taut skins. Firms breasts. Gleaming, tanned stomach muscles. Wandering fingers against long tapered legs. Wet mouths and the sound of panting on the air. Whispers of grass and metal. Paradox and Poison and Cocaine and Musk in the damp air. The echo of strobe lights made patterns across the ground, and they were all children dancing on the moon. Carefully packaged, gum chewing time bombs.

Her thighs were pressed against a dry crumbling wall and she realised that she was shaking to the beat. Sweat rushed to the surface of her skin to be whisked away by the chill air. Her whole mind jerked. Home wasn't far, just over there, a few steps, one foot in front of the other. (*GODAMNIT, Meg- MOVE!*) and she cursed herself. Why did she always stay at the library so late? She could have borrowed the books and gone home before all this began. Mother loved to see her read, would never disturb her, except to pat her with gentle fingers as she passed around the house, cleaning, endlessly cleaning.

And now she had to go home.

Had to pass.

She started forward. One step. Two steps. Now she was passing a yellow Ferrari. It had a red candy wrapper stuck to its hood, and as she watched, it blew loose and went laughing down between the other cars.

(*Meg's coming...*)

Three more steps. A fourth. A battered VW - VW's always seem battered in your nightmares - and a grinning, arrogant Chevrolet. Smelling her. Telling. Telling them. (*don't tell, don't tell, don't tell!*)

(*Meg's coming ......*)

Waves and waves from the cars. Throbbing with the beat. Telling. Her scent would go wafting over and they would look up. The young ones.

She began to walk faster, tripping over her own feet. She was nearer the doors now, and the music was louder in her bloodstream. They hadn't seen her. Maybe she could slip by unnoticed. She had never done it before, but maybe this time. This time.

A girl stood by the steps, drink in hand. She was smiling at the man in front of her. He threw his arm around her shoulders and Meg could see the perfect curve of her navel, the soft swell of her stomach, could see the white camisole she wore slashed to her waist.

The red candy wrapper danced on in the breeze. The girl had a scar on her left ankle. and her boyfriend wore a raw silk coat. She shifted her weight from one golden Roman sandal to the other.

The wrapper paused as if measuring the distance.

Meg's blood sang.

The wind smiled.

Her breasts shrank back against her ribcage, back pedalled desperately against her. Six more steps. Now she was half-way across. If she could just pass them. (*I'll go to church this Sunday, Mom, I promise, just let me pass*).

It jerked and fled a few feet in the air. A pause. Meg's heart thudded painfully in her chest. Gently, the wrapper settled on the woman's ankle, covering the scar. She stamped to free herself of the annoying clot of paper. It hung on, sticky and malevolent. Meg's body fled to her eyelashes for solace. (*Because I've got blue eyelashes, yes...they'll let me through...because my eyelashes are part of them...I use Max Factor eyeshadow every morning...don't you understand? See...blue...a supplication, a prostration, an offering...*)

The girl plucked the wrapper off her ankle. Her dark eyes caught Meg, swaying in the breeze, three heavy books beneath her arm. She saw the thin dress, the flat feet. She didn't see the blue. Laughing, she drew back her hand and flung the wrapper in Meg's direction. And Meg came alive and she ran, and she ran, and she ran, hearing the crescendo of the library clock behind her.

****

She made a decision about her life. Something had to brighten corners that she saw as dark and dim. At school, the crowd looked normal. Not like her, but safer. They wore T-shirts and trainers and their scrubbed faces were not different from her own. Were they? Surely she was part of them too. Her fantasies tripped up in her dreams and she lay awake, listening to her mother scratching the back of her throat, that croaking noise (*like the lizards, the croaking ones back whee she came from*) filling the house. She would go to Façade, light up the dance floor. The most beautiful boy would come and dance with her, snake hips and thick eyelashes. She would be like them. There would be explanations, apologies. *We knew you were one of us*, they would say. *We were waiting for you.*

****

"It's twenty to get in."

The doorman stared at the girl. She was cigarette ash. Ready to fall, smouldering. She stood before the belly of Façade, her pores wide open. The ground shifted hard beneath her. He handed her a ticket. It was a slice of brick in her hand. Mom would be mad if she found out, so mad that Meg, her good girl wasn't at the library. She had wavered at the last minute, but she had heard the music.

> *It takes two ta make a thing go right*
> *It takes two ta make it outta sight*
> *Said it's time ta get*
> *Said it's time ta get*
> *Said it's time ta get*
> *Funky!*

Too late to turn back from temptation. A party of twelve youths stood behind her. Checks, stripes and impatient smells. One spoke.

"Hey, get a move on will ya? You're in the way you ski..."

(oh no, not that. I'm one of you. Don't call me...)

Meg was inside. It stretched long before her. The walls were hot, pink, the marble floor a roll of black shadow. A man walked past, leaving a drink in her hand. She stared until it was swept from her by another. The sound of breaking glass drowned in the music. She couldn't believe how loud it was. Panic hit her, and she turned to leave, but the crowd pushed at her, and not daring to swim upstream she found a bar stool and clung to it. Across the floor she recognised the girl from the night before. She looked back indifferently and danced on. Meg let herself smile, at first tremulous, then, as the girl continued to wave her arms to the beat, her lips rolled off her gums in joy. She was in. She looked at them.

The multitude was self-absorbed, yet they moved in unison, every hip part of a larger truth. Predestined choreography. Shifted golden sands and skin aglow. Flesh mottled with strobe. Meg could feel the beat in her throat and thighs. Slowly her heart began to beat time.

> Said it's time ta get
> Said it's time ta get
> Funky!

"What are you drinking?"

The bartender was cut from a Chippendale catalogue. Square jawed, corn coloured hair, set square teeth.

"I don't drink..." she faltered.

"Aw c'mon girlie. I'll make you my special."

She watched him pick up a glass, let the small of her back settle against the spidery edges of the stylised stool. A dog was pacing at its owner's feet, whining. Bones jutted at odd angles through fur and it's eyes were lined with kohl. It's owner lifted it off the floor and danced with it as the animal tucked its hindquarters inwards. Meg turned back to the bartender and blinked. He was opening cans of maraschino cherries. He slopped three into a blender, adding drops from small containers. He was slicing the cherries into halves against his sharp jaw, his white shirt splattered with vermillion drips. She stared, trying to understand how he was doing it. Behind his shoulder two women kissed, chewing at each other's lips, their hips rubbing against each other. One leaned forward and took a handful of hair from her partner's head, the rip of scalp impossibly audible. Meg put her hand to her mouth and retched as she watched the first reach between her legs and store the hair in her underwear. The couple smiled at her and the dog howled. One of the women touched her.

"Keep this for me."

It was a tiny yellow box.

"Oh yes, but-"

The bartender thrust a pitcher at her as the women disappeared into the throng.

The lights went off.

In the swirl of the dark, Meg stood perfectly still. The club was a meaty silence.

Bass shattered into colours before her eyes, orange, green, red.

"PAAAAAAAAARTY!!!"

The music crashed once more into the face of the crowd as they turned to their frenzied task. A raised dais stood on the dance floor, a lone spotlight trained onto its surface. The chant began.

(ESTA LOCA! ESTA LOCA!)

Before the hungry mass he stood arms outstretched. Then leaping, twisting, he became the beat, caressed by soiled white spandex. His long red curly hair was pulled back severely. He had expressionless eyes, black as the tolling of a bell. His face was painted white, the mouth thin, wet, lined with purple. Black hieroglyphics scrawled over his cheekbones. his tongue flecked out as if to taste the music. Orange and purple rags hung from his wrists and ankles. Occasionally he would pause in his wild abandon and march on the spot, his body quivering. He played the mannequin, counting his fingers, moving his head from side to side in curious robotic fashion, oblivious of the roar of the crowd beneath him. And then the wilding would begin once more. As he leaped high into the air Meg felt her body jolt. She tried to catch his eyes but they were empty, blank, as he gazed at a fixed point ahead of him. They were as still as his body was alive, insane with the dance, the dance, the dance. Soaring, shifting, his genitals were tucked away so they could not obscure the smooth fit of the fabric.

(My God, he's an angel, an angel, Momma if you could see me now)

He was flying now - flying - they were over roof tops, gardens, all God's things

(It takes two ta make....)

Amen.

Pounding, screaming, leaping, twirling

(a thing go right)

Amen.

(BOOM BOOM BOOM let's go back to your room)

Ah Ah Amen.

(So we can do it all night)

Amen

Oh-Oh-OH

(So I can make you feel right)

Yes. Yes. Yes.

Sweat pouring. Bathing. Across the madman's body.

The lights were black and he was gone.

She clung to the dais, exhilarated. People were leaving. He was the climax, the crowd had come. She followed the movement towards the door. Outside, she wanted to shout in exhilaration. She had done it and if Mom could have understood she would have been proud.

The yellow box fell to the pavement. She opened it. Stared with disbelief. She turned and vomited against the side of the wall, into a pile of garbage bags that stank and festered.

The nipple glinted up at her, plump and fresh, like a fruit.

Through its centre a golden hoop, stained with rust.

Meg lived for the nights. She had to find him. The memory of his face haunted her dreams, even when she was awake. She would steal from her classes and run to the toilets, and shutting the door behind her, fondle herself harshly, rubbing her crotch against the securely locked door. Her orgasms were powerful things, leaving herself sobbing and furious with herself at the weakness of her flesh. Even as the sophisticated spasms crept through her, her thoughts were absurd. She wanted him to be her boyfriend. They would marry and he would dance and she would study, support him, believe in his art. She walked the dance floor, questioning, endlessly. She forgot her paralysing shyness. Someone. Someone had to know. Who was he? A tall youth promised to tell her and she didn't protest as she knelt between his legs watching him unzip himself. His genitals smelt like rubber as she moved forward, swallowed him, his movements jerky and careless against her cheeks. She swallowed like a pro and went for another cherry drink when he laughed at her unanswered questions. The dancer's androgyny worked on her blood. Meg shook. Her hands, her lips. Shook. And still feverishly, she passed through the place, asking,

(Can you help me, there's a dancer, do you know his name?)

When he was onstage she subsided, gaunt, to the very edge of the dais, drinking his *(estalocaestalocaestaloca)* madness, longing for his empty eyes. They all knew her now. She saw them smile as she stepped through the crowd. But it was a secret. Nobody could tell her. She was fascinated. With their rules and the etiquette of the place. They only called him The Dancer. *Do you wanna know who The Dancer is? We all wanna know.* She would find out for them. She would know. She would be the keeper of the secret. The blue of her mother's Bible drove her out of her mind. The gentle cleaning, the moan of the clock *(too slow, too slow)* worked at her. Her body shrank, skin to the bones, the hair to the scalp. And she shook. Waited.

****

The impervious walls of the library greeted her as people tried not to recoil from her burning face. She was skeletal. The graffiti reached out to embrace her, delighted.

It was good to have a friend. In one fist she crumpled her exam results. She ran her fingers over stacks of books and lifted down a heavy encyclopedia. She sagged under its weight. It was so heavy as she was so *(TIRED o tired lord yes)* but she had to study. Maybe he visited *(hung out, baby, hung out)* in the library somewhere, near it *(please o please)*. Blue smeared across her face. She took down the books, methodically, piled them behind on the floor. *(Is there a Bible, yes give me one. It takes two - ha ha ha very funny - wonderful, wonderful, wonderful, FUNKY...)*

NO AYDS PLEASE
NO NOISE PLEASE

She hugged the books to her chest and began to rock on the floor, the rows of shelves high above her *(esta loca, esta loca)* and watched her tears soak into the page *(like his sweat, yes, sweating leaping, watch him)*. The mascara streaked into them and fell across the leather covers *(is blue the colour of his eyes never hurt me cry and even Jesus wept why shouldn't I)*. Her nails fell on the page, jagged, accusing white crescents. She picked them up as they fell and put them on her tongue, tasting herself. He would come to her now, use the rags at his wrists to wipe the tear *(the rags at his wrists silky soft swish yes the beat mmm)* wipe the dust off the dictionaries *(esta loca, esta loca loca loca NO AYDS NO RAYDS PUH -LEEZE I'm a good girl - uh-huh)*.

The librarian grinned at the clock. Time to go. God, he loved pretty women. And they were all over him these days. What was that witch doing back there? Not his problem. His shift was finished. New time.

The humming sounded in his head as he lifted his tote bag and signed out. Tote bag full of soiled spandex, orange and purple rags. He took off his cap as he stepped into the night. A girl walking past smiled at the fire in his curls.

The click of his heels echoed on the pavement as a blood red candy wrapper danced after him in the wandering breeze.

Leone Ross

HEAVEN CAN WAIT

I cannot wait for heaven for
my service is the revolution
my congregation the masses
my ministry the youth of today-
the flowers of tomorrow-
the freedom fighters to replace me.
I was baptised into political education
and born again in the struggle.

My trinity is:commitment
organisation and humility
Our salvation is liberation in
Pan-Africanism.
Our slogan: "Don't turn the other cheek.
Make heaven on earth."
That is the mission,
To fulfil or betray.

heaven can wait....

Ama Biney

THE BLACK THE WHITE
AND THE BLUE

He's an East End lad East End Ed
East End born East End bred
see his muscles have a feel
made in England made of steel
East End lad East End lad
square jaw gift of the gab
packs a punch to find a clue
see his victim black and blue

Black man Asian man
flew from the East to East Ham
sun don't rise in East End cell
where Bangladesh meets English hell
hate mail dog crap
midnight petrol bomb attack
sticks and stones and PAKI GO HOME
make his street a no go zone

When Asian man dials 999
covered in blood of racist crime
police arrive police arrest
the Asian man and kick his chest
and 666 the beast walks free
and The Sun won't print what The Sun won't see
BOYS IN BLUE BEAT BLACK MAN
coz Blue protects Blue whenever Blue can

PC White adds a stripe to his arm
the man suffers grievous bodily harm
they try to charge him for assault
"We had to restrain him it's all his fault"
PC Edward White just an East End lad
with a chip on his shoulder of which he's proud
gotta be a hard nut come what may
so no-one will ever guess   that he's gay

105

East End lad West End fag
same man different drag
West End fag West End fag
remembers the words of his East End dad
"This country's gone downhill over the years
and d'ya know why?" "Why dad?" "Niggers and queers...
Bring back hanging that's what I say...
you could walk the streets without fear in my day..."

West End Eddie enters the club
looking attractive looking for love
his eye lashes lowered his eye lingers long
on the man in the corner muscular bronze
At dawn when they leave it's erogenous zones
that they have on their minds not the sticks and the stones
of the gang that attack not the stainless steel
of their knives "You queer bastards how does this feel?"

East End lad went up West
now oppressor now oppressed
couldn't see in light of club
his big bronze man had Asian blood
East End blood on West End street
what will he say to his friends on the beat?
He can paint the town red but at dawn he'll pay
with a scar on his body that says "I'm gay"

West End fag West End fag
stabbed in the back by an East End lad
son of a racist left him for dead
boy in blue is covered in red
Black man Asian man
kisses his lips and holds his hand
NIGGER PAKI QUEER
When will we walk the streets without fear?

Patience Agbabi

106

FALSE CELEBRATION OF SELF

And
what will you
tell the children

When they
come to realise
that their rich heritage
is buried
in the very Britishness
of the Queens crown
in the very paste
which
brick on brick
make tall museums
and halls
stand tall

And what will you
tell them

When they no longer
bend to blend
no longer
choose to
play fool to ketch wise

or play, humble
as though they are
mere visitors
to British shores

Their Blackness
is in the
very Morris dance
of Britishness

So
Why do you
call them stranger
now
that your very
centrality
is based on their misery

There has been a
multi cultural celebration
and they
have not been invited

There has been a
multi cultural celebration
and they
have not
been invited

NO

You cannot be excused from the table
just because you sport
an anti racist badge

White lines still
make the boundaries
of where those
with melanin in their skin
can live

NO
My friend

You cannot be excused from the table
just because you have put
a penny in the Oxfam can

Still

We stand peripheral
in our own kingdoms

Blackamoor and nigger
have simply been
tipp-exed over
to make way for
non-white and ethnic minority
terminology

When will they
be able
to define themselves
for themselves?

Here
I stand watching

Pure Black veins
dilate
allowing the surge
of history's twisted serum

In
Concrete jungles
they are taught
how to hate
their very selfs
As they thumb
through books
in search of
an absent face

Their face

They
learn how easy it is
to read, memorise
and internalise
branded messages and lies

Until
they finally
believe
that this image is truth
this image is truth
this image is truth

And it is difficult
to disbelieve what has been
written

Here
I stand watching

The many
who have disregarded Africa
as if they have been
hit on the head
with some
kind of coconut complex

There has been a
multi cultural celebration
and they
have not been invited

There has been a multi cultural celebration
and they
have not been invited

Mother Africa
stoops
weak with
her slashed wrists

Her fate
a slow slow death
Piles of bodies
make monumental messages

The life of a Black
is equal to the life of a fly

There has been a
multi cultural celebration
and they
have not been invited

and

Chink

there goes another penny
in the Oxfam can
towards
a clear conscience

Paula Sorhaindo

LAND OF MAKE BELIEF

Visualise this no racial problems
we all got together to finally solve them
no prejudice to hold us back now
blacks pro white and whites pro black now
babies conceived by mixed people
helping close the gap cos we all are equal
at last a unified nation
standing side by side in true celebration
new relations between the races
family photo albums with different colour faces
but wait! Before you sigh with relief
Welcome to my land of make belief.

Drugs are now never used
no more addicts are being abused
by crack, cos it left people dead
now no need for the phrase Coke head
a killer everyone resists
users and pushers no longer exist
no more houses of ruin
having junkies do the things that they were doing
no dealings or making profits
no business men using drugs to line their pockets
hypocrisy you know the score
saying that it's wrong then coming back for more
authorities, I point a finger at you
you never did as much as you could do
we know why, don't play us stupid
drugs were a tool and BOY did you use it
COCAINE a distant memory
once a potent force but now a beaten enemy
wait! Cos we haven't achieved
Welcome to my land of make belief.

Welcome to my land of make belief my friend
it's not real it's just pretend
maybe it's a perfect point of view
but things are wrong so what are we gonna do
when the chat is over and we're over the chat

are we one day gonna look back
PROUDLY! At what we achieved
or will it just remain a flight of FANTASY!

All nations assisting each other
developing trust for one another
armed forces no need for guns
war no more - peace for everyone.
One religion - a God for you and me
now on knees we pray to be free
no famine - food for everyone
African children playing in the sun
one language so we all understand
sharing and caring for the brother-hood of man
Dreams-dreams-dreams, they're only dreams see
maybe one day they'll be reality
for now a seed in the mind
hoping to develop with the course of time
so it remains a fantasy.
Welcome to my land of make belief.

Jude The Observer

THE RAP-TRAP

Black
young and gifted
your politics shifted
used to be a giver
now you're floating down the river
like driftwood
sold your soul for a deal
the big black badman
sexist appeal
get real
not so long ago they used to lynch ya
now that you've sung well-hung
get the picture?
Rap to rape
might be your fantasy escape
but look what they did to the ape

in the RAP-TRAP

Slack
went the rhymes
when you signed on the dotted line
dot dot dot
now you can't find rewind
heard it on the grapevine
rape-line BT urinal
you pimp your sisters on vinyl
Black
man rapper
Black man ragga ragga Shabba
did you lay down that track
or was it Abba?
Money Money Money
you're a slave
to the lyrical trade
'cept now you're getting paid

in the RAP-TRAP

Snap
went the trap
when you starred in the video show
3D went your stereo ego
rich man gangsta
shooting up the hood
you're wading through the river
of your mother's and your sister's
menstrual blood
and there's no looking back
and you're selling your brothers your slack
rhymes with free-base
Uncle Tom with a hard-on
disgracing the race

in the RAP-TRAP

Patience Agbabi

AN OBSCURE WITNESS

As she arrived at the stadium gates, Bose heard the cries and looked round sharply. In the distance, she thought she recognised the thin figure crouched over the form on the ground near the bushes. She watched, frozen, as the moonlight revealed a pale hand clenched around an object, raised up and down as it repeatedly struck short, vicious blows. And then a thin sharp sound that sounded like a small animal screaming, unnerved her. Her fumbling hands unlocked the large gates that led into the empty stadium that she cleaned every morning. She ran in. It was Lucy's boyfriend, and he had just killed her, she thought hysterically.

The week before, she had noticed both of them by the prison, near the stadium. Early morning cleaners like herself could be excused if seen at that time, but she knew that Lucy was unemployed and the boyfriend was definitely not a cleaner. She was more than certain that he was a drugs dealer. She knew he was the leader of the gang of young 'layabouts' on her council estate. Nobody had to tell her then, that Lucy's boyfriend, the boy with the pale face and red thatch was the magnet.

It saddened her to see Lucy in his company. Once when she chanced to meet them together, Lucy said a cheery hello to Bose while he just stared at her unblinkingly. He was like a venomous, quiet snake, waiting to strike.

As the boy led Lucy away, he had suddenly looked in Bose's direction and she had dodged to the side although it seemed to her that his eyes slid, like ice over her heavy body. Both soon disappeared into the damp morning. Bose feared him.

She knew that having her job was risky but it paid. She had been grateful to have been picked by the cleaning agency and given this regular spot of cleaning in the administration block in the stadium, four hours daily, at three pounds and hour. But the area was so lonely that no-one would hear her scream if she were ever attacked. On one side of the stadium was the prison and on the other side was a long stretch of lonely road on which she travelled to work alone or with her partner, Nike, each day.

She had seen a man the previous week tracing and retracing his steps near that towering dead-end block of concrete that shielded the hulking prison. Bose's sharp eyes had instantly picked him out as she arrived for work. It had surprised her when, as she continued watching from behind the locked stadium gates, Lucy appeared from the direction of the prison with a thick set man whose hand was wrapped around her waist. Bose saw the man furtively pass something to Lucy's boyfriend and then leave.

The word prostitution played around in her mind for the whole of that day. Thinking of Lucy as one had so shocked her that she had been quiet. Nike had noticed.

"What's wrong, Auntie," she asked her.

The eyes in her plump round face still bright, unmarked by the pressures of living in a Western society, fixed themselves on Bose as the older woman mopped the floor. Nike's constant anxiety irritated her. Hearing the question, she gave the floor a final swipe and grunted in reply. Nike had persisted.

"Auntie, I tire of this job. I want the agency to take me to somewhere safe."

Young women! Bose thought. If this girl were asked to produce her papers she would have nothing to show but a six-month visa yet here she was talking about picking and choosing jobs!

"Be satisfied with what God has given you," she muttered in reply.

"Not much Auntie!" Nike had exclaimed.

"Are you saying God has done nothing for your life?"

Bose stopped working, one hand on waist, leaning on the broom handle and glared at Nike with red, puffy eyes. Her cleaning partner looked defiant.

"I think there is more he can give. This job is not safe."

Bose ignored her - she knew that at least that part was true. They had continued to work steadily until eight when the supervisor, an English woman, younger than both of them, came to inspect their work. She always arrived at eight o' clock and stayed only for ten minutes after giving the place cursory checks.

"Good girls," she said as she marked the time sheet to be passed on to the agency. "Hope you haven't had any problems. Any more weirdos hanging around here?" Her large grey eyes flicked around the rooms as she talked - a routine question which required no answer.

****

As she shivered in the office her mind replayed the horror she had just witnessed, Bose remembered that Nike would not be starting work till five-thirty today. It was still only five. The boy would have fled by the time she arrived. She dropped her duster and sat down as her mind travelled to the first day she had met Lucy. It had been the day when Bose had misplaced her passport on her way back home from the lawyer's office. He had told her she could be deported because her visa had expired.

"Is there nothing to be done?" Bose leant over and grasped the edge of his desk, her tense knuckles turning red.

He relaxed back in his chair as if watching a movie.

"No. You came with a visitor's visa and are overstaying in this country. Your only chance now is to marry a British citizen," he had replied, as she felt his eyes flow pityingly down her lumpy body. How would anyone consider marrying her at her age? Yet there was no going back - she would have to stay illegally. Too many people were relying on her back home for the little but necessary money she sent.

Lucy said she had found the passport near the dump bin at a bus stop, which is probably why no-one else had taken any notice of it, and had traced it back to her. Bose still could not see how it had fallen from her bag. She was so careful about such things. But the knock on her door a few days later, and the dark-haired English girl in a cheap tight dress holding out her passport was such a relief it would never leave her memory.

" 'ere is your passport, luv", she had said. "Traced yer through yer cousin. Has 'is address at the back. 'e gave me yer address." She said with her deep hazel eyes and generous smile.

Bose had gratefully thanked her and invited her in. Lucy accepted and even stayed for dinner, a meal of fufu and cassava leaf stew that Lucy then, and every other time she found herself at Bose's house, insisted on eating with a knife and fork. That was how their strange friendship began. It seemed like a miracle to Bose that Lucy lived with her parents on the same estate as her, because they lived so close yet had never seen each other. Although she had never been to Lucy's home, Bose knew all about 'Ma and Da' and Lucy's latest boyfriend. It was a sad time for her when she found out that Lucy had turned to drugs, like many of the other youths on the estate. It was hard to forget it was the same girl that had proudly told her she would go back to retake her 'A' Levels and then go on to university.

"I want to make something of me life. Ma and Da don' understand, Bose." (Lucy pronounced her name as 'Bow -Say' - but Bose never corrected her). She laughed softly, then in one breath changing from one subject to another, eagerly asked Bose about Nigeria. "I'd like ter go one day ter Africa and see for meself." Her eyes narrowed as she looked pensive. "See all them animals meself."

When she felt she knew her better, Bose confronted Lucy, about the drug-taking, when she came to the flat. It was hard not to notice that the girl's face had turned gaunt and her formerly smooth skin unhealthily pale and covered in tiny red spots. But Lucy became evasive and looked away from Bose's eyes. For the first time since Bose met her, Lucy refused a meal and made excuses to leave.

That was the last time she had seen her. And now all Bose could remember was that scream. She fell on her knees and started praying to God. Her words were fast and unintelligible as she beat her chest with a tight fist. She stood up and in a calmer state, began gathering her cleaning equipment. Her prayers had released her. *Do nothing and say nothing.* The words kept repeating themselves in her head. *Do nothing and say nothing.* If she told the police, they would report her to immigration and then ... she didn't dare think about it. What about Lucy? Another voice whispered. Lucy was dead. Bose started to work.

Nike absolved from the task of being a witness to the evil, came in at five-thirty. Bose examined her bland expression and knew she had seen nothing. As she suspected, the boy must have already made his exit. She began to think all manner of things. Paranoid and hysterical thoughts swept through her mind and she began to shiver again. They finished work at eight o'clock and waited for the supervisor. She was unusually late. Nike began fretting.

"I have said I don't like this job, Auntie. See how late she will be and they will not pay us money for this, o."

Bose's brain was crammed with images. All she wanted to do was to go to church.

"Are you all right, Auntie?" asked Nike.

She nodded quickly and looked away. Nike's curious eyes were still on her when the supervisor arrived at eight-thirty - half an hour late. She looked distressed.

"Girls, girls. Something has happened. There's been a terrible killing near here. Some poor girl has been mutilated and her body dumped behind the bushes. The police are all over the place." Her face changed as she eyed them expectantly. Bose felt her heart twist as the supervisor asked: "Did either of you see anything?"

"No," was Bose's strangled reply. "We see nothing!"

"In that case, we're clear. The management would like to stay out of this. I can't look around today. I'm sure everything is fine. Go home now."

As they turned to go she called them back, her face serious. "Girls, we will try to avoid it happening, but if the police need to question you, you have to be available, all right?"

They nodded. Bose felt her body grow warm then cold. Her heart started pumping so fast that she felt faint.

"Are you all right, Bose?" The supervisor laid a hand on her arm as she swayed.

"Yes," she whispered as she tried to pull her mind together. She felt like falling on the ground and crying. Her face, as young as Lucy's, closely examined her.

"Go home and rest. But both of you should be prepared," she warned.

They came out to witness the busy scene outside. Both gasped as they watched the blood soaked, swaddled body being carried into the ambulance.

"Who killed her?" A subdued Nike asked blankly as they left the scene. "What will we do now? I don't want the police to look for me. They will ask for my papers," she wailed. "What will we do, Auntie? I say I don't like this job, and I mean it. I must run away today. I cannot see the police. Auntie, what will we do?"

"I don't know," answered Bose wearily. "Go home and pray."

The next day, Bose did not go to work. In the afternoon she left her flat and went to church. Her eyes as as she walked through the estate strayed everywhere in search of the 'layabouts' and their gang leader. None were in sight. Yet the estate was busy. Lucy's death had been reported on the news. A crowd curiously surveyed reporters and photographers stationed by her parents block.

For days, she followed the newspapers and television that told about the search for the killer. Lucy's smiling face, without makeup, appeared innocent on the television and newspaper front pages. She waited for the police, yet prayed for them not to arrive. As long as the search for the boy went on, the need to question her and Nike grew.

Bose started going for night vigils in her church as well as her after work session. All night prayers soothed both her guilt and fear. Especially when it seemed that the police might never contact her - the newspapers reported they had a suspect.

They must have caught the boy she thought. But her daily scanning of newspaper and television never mentioned him. She found out why when she left the church three nights later. There he was, amongst the crowd staring at Lucy's house. Their eyes met. He still stared at her unblinkingly, the way she remembered when she first saw him with Lucy but this time she was sure that a slight smile curved one side of his mouth. Acknowledgement that they had both known Lucy - and that he knew Bose too, more than she knew.

Stella Oni

WRITERS PROFILES

Chris Abani
Chris Abani was born in Nigeria. He has a BA in English Language and Literature and an MA in Society, Culture and Gender Studies. He has worked variously as a civil servant and arts worker and currently teaches creative writing. He is the author of three novels and a collection of poetry, *Masters of the Board* (Delta 1983), *Sirocco* (Delta 1987), *A Quite Anger* (Erusi 1996) and *Sun Dancer* (JAP & Erusi 1996). He won the 1983 Delta Fiction Award and the WAWA (West African Writers Association) for Best New Novel in 1984. He is currently the Information Technology editor for *Calabash*, a publication for writers of African and Asian descent. He lives in London and also plays the piano and saxophone.

Adisa (One who makes his meanings clear)
This P.O.E.T. (Practitioner Of Enlightened Talk), Adisa, hailing from St. Vincent was born and raised in Luton. He spent 7 years working as a signwriter and in his spare time moved with the Sovereign sound system where he first got a taste for performing in front of large crowds as he often toasted over the mic. During 1992, he found himself becoming more involved in community organisations based in London which fuelled his desire to know more about our history and in turn made him more in tune with himself. He is now based in London and changed from chatting on the mic in dance halls to using poetry as a means of self expression. His primary desire is to help bring poetry to a mass audience. Adisa won the title of Best New Performance Poet 1994 in a national competition. He studies Sam Tu Dang, a physical discipline that helps him retain his focus and helped him compile his first book, *Seven Inches of Love*.
"Each time that he takes the stage, he delivers a potent, commanding performance of insightful and strong poetry."
Artrage magazine

Patience Agbabi
Patience Agbabi is a British-born Nigerian poet, perfomer and workshop co-ordinator. She is an international poet educated at Pembroke College, Oxford and the Performance Poetry Circuit, London. She has toured the UK, Europe and South Africa. Her work has been published in several anthologies including *The Virago Book Of Wicked Verse*. Her first collection, *R.A.W.*, was published by Gecko Press in 1995. She is a member of the poetry pop group, ATOMIC LIP, and is currently writing a collaborative show, Four Women, with Adeola Agbebiyi and Dorothea Smartt.

120

"I write because I've always had that desire to collate and arrange my disparate thoughts and then re-release them. Every poem is a remix. All of my poems are orally conceived even my concrete pieces, since I rarely differentiate between poetry and music.
For me, poetry is music."

Joan Anim-Addo

Joan Anim-Addo is a writer and teacher born in Grenada, educated in the Caribbean and London. She lives in London dividing her working time between teaching and writing. Her poems and short stories have been published by the *Women's Press*, *Poetry Now* and magazines including *New Impact* and *Scratch*. Her non-fiction book, *Longest Journey: A History of Black Lewisham* was published in 1995. Joan Anim-Addo edits *Mango Season*, the magazine of the Caribbean Women Writers' Alliance. She edited the anthology *Mango An' Spice* and the collection of literary essays *Framing The Word: Gender and Genre in Caribbean Women's Writing*. Her essays and articles appear in a number of magazines and journals.

Uju Asika

Uju Asika is a 21 year old woman born in Nigeria and raised in the U.K. She has a B.A. in English from University College London.
"I could be regarded as a 'cultural mulatto' (to borrow Christopher Okigbo's term) although I would never describe myself as anything other than Nigerian. I am passionate about literature, especially poetry and hope to pursue a career in writing both critically and creatively. I am also hooked on art, film, drama and music, music, music - anything from hip hop to Handel. I draw the line at slash metal and nasal country ballads!"

Ama Biney

"My poems are largely based on my political convictions and outlook; my observations on human beings and a commitment to see a change in the world. They came out of a period between 1987-1992, when I was part of the Jenako Black Writers group based in Dalston, London. My Masters degree is in Government and Politics of West Africa which was later followed by attaining a Post Graduate certificate in Computer Training. Since then, I have been working in two fields: as computer trainer and lecturer in History and African and Caribbean Studies. Currently, my poetry has been taken over by my writing on social and political issues for two journals, *African World Review* and *Southern Africa Political Economic Monthly*."

Sue Brown

Born in Birmingham of Jamaican parents, Sue is a Video Production Trainer by profession, freelancing in and around the West Midlands. She wrote her first poem, *Jazz Jamaica*, in 1993, then *Respect Due* - a personal gift for her sisters and close friends. Within months of writing these, she was asked to take part in the renowned Birmingham Readers & Writers Festival in 1994 where she performed her work to reggae and jazz music. Since then, she has taken part in various events including Dub & Beyond in Germany where she appeared with Jean Binta Breeze and Linton Kwesi Johnson. She is currently exploring linking her new 'awareness in writing skills' to the visual work of video and theatre. Her latest achievement has been to work in collaboration with the New Jamaican Arts Exhibition where her work went on display in the Birmingham Museum & Arts Gallery. The list is still growing...

Jean Buffong

Jean was born in Grenada. As well as an established novelist, Jean also writes poetry, short stories and plays, mainly inspired by everyday happenings, but its to her 'paradise' Grenada that she returns for inspiration for her novels. Her novels, *Jump Up and Kiss Me* and *Under the Silk Cotton Tree* (Women's Press) depict the love she has for Grenada...language, food, in other words a huge slice of the Grenadian culture. Her childhood home is never far away from her existence; that is evident in her latest novel, *Snowflakes in the Sun*; a book of England's stories told within a Grenadian setting. Jean's work can also be found in *The Women's Press Book of Myths and Magic, Hearsay,* a book of poetry, and *Mango an' Spice,* an anthology by the Caribbean Women Writers Alliance. Jean is the co-editor of the anthology *Just A Breath Away* and the writer of the foreword to the English publication *Sisterfire*, an American book of fiction and poetry by Black women. Apart from being in full time employment and her work as a writer, Jean is an active community worker, including chairperson of the Afro-Caribbean Educational Project Women's Centre and the welfare officer of the West Indian Standing Conference. Jean is now working on her fourth novel.

Bernardine Evaristo

Anglo/Nigerian writer, Bernardine Evaristo is the author of *Lara,* a novel-in-verse, (Angela Royal Publishing) 1997 and *Island of Abraham,* a poetry collection, (Peepal Tree Books 1994). Her writing has appeared in eight anthologies and many magazines and she was co-editor of *Blackwomen Talk Poetry Anthology* in 1987. Her theatre plays toured England and Europe and she has lived in Spain and Turkey. She regularly gives public performances of her work and teaches creative writing. She lives in London.

Jude The Observer

Jude formed the rap group Free Speech in the summer of 1992 when he opened the Apples & Snakes 8th mid-summer Poetry Festival. He invited a singer and trumpet player to perform with him and so the foundation of Free Speech was laid. Their free flowing acappella set was a huge success and as a group, they have toured England, Germany, Spain and Italy. Jude has performed with poets Lemn Sissay, Patience Agbabi and Jalal Nuriddin of The Last Poets. Jude's poetic work has been described as

"...coming over all Gil Scott Heron in style and substance,"
Blues and Soul magazine.

Angela Harvey-Smith

This eloquent poetess from North London has made steady waves on the London performance poetry scene. Writing poetry since childhood, she chose to remain behind the scenes for years; but a driving sense of purpose brought her to the stage in late 1994. Her *Poetry in Music* performance is accompanied by a ten member band! The effect truly has to be seen to be believed. After a year appearing at various prestigious theatres and festivals; supporting community arts and justice campaigns, she has commanded respect and admiration, receiving awards to that effect. Angela describes herself as 'an environmentally friendly humanitarian who is pro Black.' She says,

"The pen and the page are my oldest friends,
helping me to bridge the gaps in the puzzles of life."

Pete Kalu

Having been brought up on books more than TV, I enjoy my writing even though the problems I encounter sometimes frazzle my brain. I seem to be finding it harder and harder to write poetry as I get older. I've been doing them (poems) for ten years now. It's not the initial idea that's hard - it's the teasing out of that idea into a poem. For this I find writing workshops - where I can throw ideas around with other writers and get their opinion - invaluable.

Chukwunyere Kamalu

"I am a writer, freelance lecturer and administrator as well as a scientist. I have a Ph.D in soil conversation and am also a musician. I have published a book on African religions and Philosophy, *Foundations of African Thought* (Karnak House 1990). I have another book on this topic, due out in 1996, entitled, *Person, Divinity and Nature*, to be published by Karnak House. I am currently writing my first novel, *Kandace's Dream*. As a musician, I have recorded some of my compositions, produced with the band IFA, which I founded with singer and choreographer, Lati Saka, who is also a co-writer on one of them. I lecture in Black Studies at the University of Reading and was a visiting lecturer in African Art and Belief Systems at the London Institute at Camberwell School of Art."

Hannah Kema Foday

Hannah Kema Foday is a 26 year old woman born in Sierra Leone. She has a degree in French and English from Fourah Bay College, Sierra Leone. In 1993-94 she held a Liberal Arts Fellowship at Kalamazoo College, Michigan, USA. She returned to Sierra Leone to teach English and French but came to England in 1994 because of the 'rebel war'. She now lives in London with her husband and works at the University of London in the Examination and Assessment Council. She has a great interest in women's issues and in the development of her country.

Bev Miller

Sensee: Rap Artist, fledgling writer and performance poet.

Stella Oni

Stella Oni was born in Britain of Nigerian parentage. She has a BA in Linguistics and African Languages from the University of Benin, Nigeria. Stella has contributed to various magazines including Pride, Candace, Concord Lifestyle, Classique, West Africa, Writers Monthly, newspapers such as Black Briton, The Weekly Journal and Calabash. She was London Editor for Mister, a gentleman's monthly based in Nigeria. She contributed an essay, *A Conversation with Yvonne Brewster, Artistic Director for Talawa Theatre* in the anthology, *Six Plays by Black and Asian Women Writers* (Aurora Metro Publications). Her short story, Simi, appears in *Sojourners*, an anthology of New Writing by Africans in Britain. In 1992, she won an Award for Services within the community, given by The Contact Club. Stella has just finished a crime novel, *Deadly Shadows* and is presently studying for an MSc in Information Systems and Technology.

Olusola Oyeleye

Olusola Oyeleye is a writer and director working in theatre, opera and radio. Contributions to publications include *Passion: Discourse on Blackwomen's Creativity* (Urban Fox Press), *New Robes For MaShulan* (Urban Fox Press), *Open Eyes* (Karnak House) London 1995 Regional Anthology (Poetry Now). She has written short films and the libretti to two operas. Stage plays include, *The Miracle Child; Many Voices, One Chant* and *Tribes*. The play, *Mure-Mure*, the play, *That Sings*, was highly commended by the Lloyds Bank Theatre Challenge for New Plays for Young People. She has received the following awards: Arts Council Trainee Producer an English National Opera (1989-90); BP Young Director's Award (1987); ACER Young Writer Award (1985).

Alex Pascall OBE

Alex Pascall combines his wealth of experience working in communities throughout Britain with his expertise as an oral historian, broadcaster, musician and raconteur. In the 1996 New Year's Honours Alex was awarded an OBE for 'services to community relations.' He was born in Grenada and came to Britain in 1959, where he has since run the Notting Hill Carnival for five years and was a founder Vice President of the Foundation for European Carnival Cities. From 1974 until 1988, Alex presented the first Black radio programme in Britain, Black Londoners, on BBC Radio London. In 1994, he researched and presented on BBC Radio 3 the series, 'A Different Rhythm,' on the influence of Black music on the British music scene. During 1995, he researched and presented for BBC Radio 2 a series about the origin of Caribbean Folk Music and a VE Day Calypso programme, shortlisted for the 1995 CRE Race in the Media Awards. The many years of Alex's research and documentation have yielded a vast historical archive on the Black presence in Britain. Alex continues to develop an understanding of life from an African Caribbean perspective through residencies and training courses in schools, libraries and festivals nation-wide, contextualising Carnival arts and encouraging a greater awareness of participants' own talents.

Roger Robinson

Roger Robinson is originally from Trinidad and now lives in England, a member of the infamous Chocolate Art poetry crew. His work is influenced by the West Indian oral tradition of chantwells, robber speeches, story telling, kaiso, soca and rapso. His performance and writing incorporates elements of all these traditional styles and written and performed in nation language. He also specialises in poetry workshops and seminars for all ages and abilities. His early work incorporated many elements of traditional West Indian folklore but his current work centres around how English society appears through West Indian eyes.

Jacob Ross

Jacob Ross has developed a distinguished reputation as a "writer's writer". His work is characterised by a distinct, lyrical and powerful narrative style that engages the reader at many levels. This Grenadian born writer has been residing in London for the past twelve years. He has worked as a freelance journalist and photographer for leading publications including *City Limits, Time Out, The Independent* and the Editor-in-Chief of *Artrage* - Britain's foremost intercultural arts magazine from 1992 to 1995. During that period, Jacob Ross also established himself as a leading commentator on Black arts and culture in Britain. His book of short stories, *Song for Simone* has been translated in German and is taught in schools in England and Austria. Jacob

Ross studied Pedagogy and Linguistics at the University of Grenoble, France. He often lectures on International Literature and has done work for bodies such as the National Association for Teachers of English, The Cultural Institute in Salsberg, The Arvon Foundation and Sheffield University. Jacob Ross' much awaited first novel is due to be published in 1997. **(FA)**

Leone Ross

Leone Ross was born in Coventry, England in 1969 to a Scottish father and Jamaican mother. Throughout most of her childhood and adolescence, Leone moved back and forth between England and Jamaica, She showed her creative ability early, writing the lyrics for her prep school's song, as well as poetry and short stories. After receiving a first class honours degree in Literature and Social Science from the University of the West Indies, Leone based herself in London to study for a masters in International Journalism at City University. She has worked as a freelance journalist, specialising in entertainment and the politics of race, gender and sexuality for a variety of women's and youth magazines. She has also worked as a researcher for London Weekend Television. Amongst others, she has interviewed the artist formerly known as Prince who inspired the title for her first novel, *All the Blood is Red*, from one of his songs. Her novel was published by ARP in September 1996.

Tumi Sephula

Tumi Mabathu Sephula was born in Natalspreit, South Africa. She is currently working in mental health with an extensive Personnel Management background. She has an honours degree from Guildhall University in Politics and Government and a postgraduate diploma in Personnel Management from the London School of Economics. She is a member of the Rhythm Writers and has been writing and performing poetry for over 6 years. She supported Toni Morrison during the tour of her book, Jazz at the Bloomsbury Theatre in 1992. Her work is due to appear in a forthcoming anthology called *Symphonies of the Soul* for the Poetry Guild .

"The poetry of Tumi Sephula
tugs at the contradictions of modern times".
West Africa magazine

Kadija Sesay

Kadija George (writes as Kadija Sesay), is from Sierra Leone, born in England. She began writing as freelance journalist to alleviate the boredom of living in Birmingham where she studied for a West African Studies degree at Birmingham University, England. She writes for several magazines about the Black British community, women and in particular

126

Black arts for publications in England, America and Africa, including a motivation column in the business newspaper, *Afroscope*. She also develops and co-ordinates publicity projects, running a company called SAKS Media with two other women. She edited the first anthology of Black women's plays, *Six Plays by Black and Asian Women Writers* (Aurora Metro) and is a tutor, for freelance journalists and creative writing. She also co-ordinates the Black Literature Development Project at Centerprise in East London and edits their publication, *Calabash*, for writers of African and Asian descent. In 1994, she was nominated as a Cosmopolitan Woman of Achievement in Creative Arts and received a Woman of Achievement Award by Candace magazine in 1996. Her personal motto is,

"Learn on someone else's time and money."

SAKS Media's motto is,

"Little by little grow the bananas."

This book is the first in five baby bananas.

Dorothea Smartt

Dorothea is the daughter of Bajan migrants who has been writing and performing her poetry for ten years at women's events, community and performance spaces. While at Centerprise Publishing Project in London, she hosted a successful series of Black women's 'Word Up Women's Cafes' and co-edited *Words From The Women's Cafe* (Centerprise 1993). In 1994, she collaborated with photographer Sherlee Mitchell to create the ICA Live Arts commission From You To Me To You. Her poetry appears in several anthologies, most recently, *Moving Beyond Boundaries* (Pluto 1995). She can be contacted at Suli Cultural Productions, Box 17, 122 Vassall Road, London SW9 6JB.

Andria Smith

Twenty-seven. Short. Redskin. Jamaican-Brummie. Born of a wonderful, short, Trelawny woman one cold, cold November. Been in London for nine years. Spent three studying for an English degree. The other six went on working in Black arts: poetry; marketing and adult education - oh yeah, and in perpetual search of goodness - you know how it goes, some days I get lucky...Writing poetry is my way of recording my discoveries on this difficult, delicate, ravaging adventure. In my spare time, I party.

"Andria Smith's poetry is rich with imagery, driven by honesty and laced with emotion." -

Lemn Sissay

Paula Sorhaindo

"I was born in Dominica and came to England in 1976. I live with my eleven year old daughter Chauntelle, my main source of inspiration. I am currently studying anti - racism in primary schools through literature and language at B.A. Hons degree level, and also work as a professional storyteller, poet and educationalist in schools and colleges. I have a healthy interest in poetry, short stories and reading on self healing and empowerment. Outside work and study, a lot of my spare time is given to volunteering my services as a youth worker and educationalist in the Black community.

Her double chained existence has shaped the person she is today. She will always find a place in her heart to enjoy the essence of life amongst all that is tragic and trash.

"Paula's poetry takes you on a journey through fascism and sexism; from living on the island of Dominica to existing in Britain."

Delroy Williams

"31, born 'n' bred in sarf London of strict pentecostal Jamaican parents whose 'spare the rod and spwoile de chil' e'tics backfired. What they did instil though, was a sense of the spiritual and manners! Been writing for the past three years mainly as a means of self-expression and understanding but recently I've taken it out to the public arena. Suppose my main influences are my family background, the fact of my experiences as a socio-cultural nomad in Britain-worldwide and a quest for personal, social and spiritual enlightenment."

VISUAL ARTISTS

Rootz

Rootz is a 31 year old Yorkshire born product of Batley Art College. Over the years he has been commissioned to illustrate and design a multitude of projects in local and national publications. His experience of working on publications propelled an enthusiasm for writing, so he has also diversified into reviewing and writing articles on Black music for music trade publications. Design though, remains at the forefront of his passion.

Salome Smeaton-Russell

Salome Russell was born in Darjeeling, India of Nepalese parents who maintained strong links with their country and culture. This has had an immense influence on her as a person and artist. She began painting in 1988, a self taught artist and poet, working with oils, pastels, water colours, gold leaf (and found objects), and also creates relief and 3D sculptures in papier mache.

"Most of my expression comes from within, but my inspiration comes from life around me today, together with my ancestral links with Nepali culture and The Himalayas (which add 'timeless' quality to my work). As a woman, it is important for me to bring all aspects of women's art and crafts together (thread work, beading and braiding), broadening the appreciation, understanding, and respect they deserve in contemporary visual arts. In my paintings of women and children, both real and imaginary, I convey the intensely powerful bond and relationships between them, and express their individual beauty and dignity. Water and shells are recurring themes in my work because it is my belief that life comes from water, and that my goddesses and gods are manifestations of the 'spirit' of Life. In 1991, I became a member of Brixton Art Gallery (Brixton Artists Collective), I became an active member of the Black Women's Artist Group within the collective and was also elected the Chairperson of the Collective. I have exhibited with the Black Women's Artists Group in exhibitions like; Mata, Red and Inner Visions, with artists like Carol Chin, Rita Keegan, Jheni Aroine and Maria Mahoney. In Nepal, art plays an integral part in women's lives (it may be in the form of murals, face-painting, house decor). Not only through the work created but in the way we participate with our whole being. Revealing complete personal involvement in the art process. I am proud of my achievements as a self-taught artist. I consider experience as my best teacher.

BURNING words
flaming IMAGES
Volume II

Short stories by
Established and New writers
of African descent
Editor: Chris Abani
Publication date: October 1997

****

BURNING words
flaming IMAGES
Volume III

Poems by
Established and New writers
of African descent
Publication date: October 1998

For more information on these books
and other SAKS Media products contact
SAKS Media
42 Chatsworth Road, London E5 OLP, England
T: +(44) 0181 985 3041   F: +(44) 0181 985 9419